UNPLUGGED

Urban Myths UNPLUGGED

Phil Healey & Rick Glanvill

Virgin

Dedicated to Frances, Yael and Ollie
and our families and friends (of friends)

First published in Great Britain in 1994 by
Virgin Books
an imprint of Virgin Publishing Ltd
332 Ladbroke Grove
London W10 5AH

A catalogue record for this book is available from the British Library.

ISBN 0 86369 897 2

Cover illustration and text illustrations by Phil Healey

Phototypeset by Intype, London
Printed and bound in Great Britain by Cox & Wyman Ltd,
Reading, Berks

cont_ents_

acknow*ledgements*

A big hello (HELLO!) to those excellent correspondents John and Sarah Hartwell of Chelmsford, where it seems everyone is at it (thanks again), Alex Stainsby for the casebook of legal gems, Jonathan A. Salt (of Plymouth) and Smiffy & co (of Portsmouth) – must be something dreadful in that naval air there, chaps! (And Smiffy – please send us your address!)

Big appreciation for the info from James 'I can't believe I believed it' Roff, Selma 'I saw it with my own eyes' Wong, Robin Eley Jones (good ideas, sir), Mark Urgent, Roy Stringer, David Newstead, D. Fleetwood, Debbie King (Mrs) and Mike Rayner.

Another big showbiz-type huzzah to the best set-up on telly, Richard Madeley and Judy Finnigan's *This Morning* (not forgetting the viewers), Radio 1's top Marks, Radcliffe and Riley (Lard), the ubiquitous Danny Baker, Liz Kershaw, Steve Wright, Robbie Vincent and the LBC listeners who set the switchboard alight with 'shaggy dog' stories, Ian Hislop and *Private Eye*, the researchers at *Good Morning With Anne and Nick* (thanks for the smashing mustard waistcoat and for treating us to JD), BBC's Radio Scotland's *The Usual Suspects*, all the local radio stations and listeners who've rung in (especially inebriated Esme from Surrey for her amiably unfathomable 'pussy' story), the *Fortean Times* (a marvellous read), the journalists who've been nice and the snobby ones – mentioning no names, even Peter Tory's – who've wanted to keep this vineyard of vintage stories about themselves.

Sincere thanks too to Deborah Orr and all the Weekend Section of the *Guardian* (don't worry, Billy – nobody noticed you missed off the punchline), Dr D. A. Pantony, Dr Jon Hobman, Dr H. B. Chipengwa, Adam Curtin for the tip-off (he should see one of those doctors we just mentioned), Iona at Acid Jazz, Annabel at MTV, Matt 'we wuz robbed!' Preston, Stan Crowther, K. D. McBride, Steve Avery, Sandra Hyman, John Hunter, Paul 'Crojo' Crome, Chris Bewis, Phil Shaw, Steve Glennon, Nathan Collins, Frosula Taliadorou, Paul Patterson, and Erica Caithness, Stuart 'Curtains' Kirkham, Big Matt 'from' Burnley, Gerry Clarke, Caroline Boucher, God the creator, M. B. Hudson, Bob Smythe, Frances Lloyd, and Frances' cousin Barbara, Tim Woolgar, Deirdre Mason, David 'have I got news for you, big boy' Powell, Satwinder Sehmi-Sober, Zoë James, Jim Judges (yes, we are mother and daughter, but don't let anyone know), Jen Cox, David Bonney, Sean from Windsor, Matthew from St Albans, Terry the cabbie, Aubrey from Barnes, David from Guildford, John from Chingford, Eileen Bethell, David Mitchell, Venetia out there in Claygate, Andrew Gibson, George Wray, Carlos Sapochnik, June Hornby, Brian Cowley, Derek F. Stoddard, Frank Desmond, Jeff Gamble, Andy Giles, Bryan Simpson, Neal Cooper (yes, they are all told by homophobics, aren't they?), Mrs Robinson (surely not *the* Mrs Robinson), Mike Campbell (London fine, thank you; how Surrey?), and, to everyone who asked: yes, we *are* having another book published . . . this one.

'Cheers, me old mucker', to our German and Hungarian translators and publishers, and to all the super people at MCI, Marc Benadout, Paul Peppiate at The Look, Knightsmove and Ginn.

Thanks to our special agent Cat Ledger for her sensitivity and self-effacement. And bringing up the rear, but not the bottom of our Xmas list, the staff and furniture at Virgin for all their support. Mal, Paul, Charlotte et al – hey, we love you guys . . .

intro*duction*

They said it couldn't be done; they said it shouldn't be done. But we didn't listen and did it anyway. So welcome again to another severe dose of mythical mockery, madcap matters and irritating alliteration in *Urban Myths Unplugged*. All your old favourite sections are there – unfortunate animals, occupational disasters, legal entanglements, stomach-churning tales of grub, disease and inebriation. But as the previous collections are translated and exported around the world it becomes clear to us that these urban myths are a global thang, baby – our first book is currently available in German and Hungarian, and there are rumours it might even be translated into proper English.

Unplugged includes contributions to the world library of popular mythology from as far afield as Australia, New Zealand, Kenya, Hungary, Poland, Russia, Canada, China, Thailand, Japan: from all four corners of the civilised globe. Yes, even Cumbria. Letters have also poured in from all over the planet providing local variations on old classic urban myths featured in our two previous books: *Urban Myths* and *The Return of Urban Myths*.

So why 'Unplugged'? Firstly, no electricity whatsoever is required to read this book – unlike some we could mention, it is quite illuminating enough by itself. And, well, seeing as the first two books were so incredibly media-friendly and we've appeared on everything from the heights of Richard and Judy and Anne and Nick to the depths of the *Daily Express* book pages, we concluded we needed something special to make sure we got on the circuit again. 'Unplugged' is a pun (well, almost) and a challenge – if not of the gauntletted variety, then at least of a fingerless mitten – to media researchers the world over to summon the courage to have us on as guests. And to make things that bit simpler, we hereby provide interview questions and smart, spontaneous responses. Honestly, what are you waiting for? Pick up the phone.

so boys, ***what is an urban myth?***

Well ***** (fill in name), urban myths are 'friend of a friend' stories of highly dubious origin and veracity. They can be funny, macabre or just plain absurd, but their most poignant asset is their universality. These stories are told worldwide wherever two or more people meet, from bar to barbeque, factory floor to boardroom. Popular mythology reflects human insecurities, and probably acts as a safety valve for the depths of the darker side we all have (well, all except Mother Teresa and Virginia Lobotomy, presumably) that are socially unacceptable in any other form. If it's supposedly 'true' and wrapped up in an hilarious escapade, it's OK to say it, no matter how non-PC, officer.

The storylines reflect basic beliefs – often conservative and bigoted – about urban life and social change. They are moralistic and heaped with retribution for those who take too many risks or flout social conventions, especially people in positions of responsibility – the higher the monkey climbs, the more he exposes, as the saying goes.

Often the endings, as in classic fairy tales, have a wicked twist to round things off. Sometimes they're akin to jokes at the expense of a social group getting above themselves – mobile phone and flash car stories abounded during the late 1980s yuppie backlash, for example.

But urban myths are just too full of coincidences, just

too perfectly rounded off, to be quite convincing. That's why the victim is always a friend of a friend; it's never the teller or anyone they actually know. The secondhand detachment of the 'friend of a friend' suggests veracity, maintains interest and suspends disbelief. And as these situations are often common to everyone, you can either see yourself there (but for the grace of God), or you can chortle at the misfortune of others.

but why *do people like them?*

Urban myths represent the art of storytelling in tabloid form. People love gossip and within popular mythology you'll find the best elements of that subversive tradition, rumour. Rumour is to urban myth what Wise was to Morecambe – nowhere near as funny, but an essential element of the performance.

There are two things in life you can rely on: gravity and people – both will always bring you down with a bump. And there's nothing we like better than to see some uppity character finally and humiliatingly called to account.

The stories also mirror the preoccupation of the tabloid press and cultural trends of the time: relationships, sex, success, failure, progress, sex, crime, health, sex, cuddly animals, horror and, last but not least, sex. It's a menu featuring everyone's favourite dishes.

how do *they spread?*

There are distinct similarities between urban myths and jokes. Everyone tells 'em whether they're aware of it or not. Both myths and jokes have dubious origins that can't be traced to one person because of the virulent nature of the passing on. And it's unlikely that their spread across countries and continents is down to one well-travelled salesman with verbal diarrhoea or a sect of urban myth evangelists. It's you and me who disseminate these stories and who keep them alive. Their content is universal and current, and the impact can be striking: perfect fodder for any conversation, any occasion.

how do *they evolve, professors?*

Once established, jokes remain fairly similar in structure and while they can alter in the individual telling – as Frank Carson would be quick to point out – the punchline remains pretty much sacrosanct. In contrast, the best urban myths constantly evolve, adapting to social changes or the vernacular details and personal references of the person relating them. Frequently, it's down to Chinese whispers. We live in an info-tech age but most of us are unable to cope with the demands on our memory – that's why we have children, and computers. But unlike computers we are creative. If we're holding court at a party and suddenly forget a detail vital to the success of a story, we tend to ad lib or improvise and another variation on the theme is born. In extreme cases, where the story has fallen flat, elements of others have been added in an effort to save face. A good example is the story concluding with the bloke who drops a full chamber pot from a window on to breakfasting guests in a conservatory. Somehow, as an epilogue, a chihuahua has begun to make a short cameo, and is sat upon and killed by the bloke who's returned to apologise.

what's funny *about that? – with respect . . .*

Nothing if you're a chihuahua. Anyway, we didn't ask to be filed under 'humour'.

you're obviously *sophisticated and cosmopolitan – so why are they 'urban' myths when some of them are about the countryside?*

Popular mythology is a window through which to view the urban outlook on life, its obsessions and prejudices: fear of the countryside as unknown territory, its over-endowment with folks of quirky ways, trigger-happy farmers and weird, unhygienic beasts – exactly like the Houses of Parliament, in other words. These aren't quaint rustic tales, they are a product of the paranoid metropolis . . .

you are brilliant *at what you do. Do people say, 'That's true – it happened to my gran . . . or was it my brother?'*

(Slipping £5 to interviewer) Some of what we now call urban myths undoubtedly have their origins in real incidents. These true stories are then retold, misheard, half-remembered and passed on, embellished with new titbits to spice things up. Some correspondents have explained the origins of specific stories that have passed into popular mythology (some, it has to be said, more persuasively than others).

Take the story of the film crew interviewing a chief of policy about a grisly murder – body parts strewn everywhere in Cromwell Street fashion – and the sound engineer piping up, 'So you've ruled out suicide, then?' This allegedly involved a Mr James Brennan, employed as a sound engineer for BBC Wales at the time (1992). He's quite happy to have made it into folklore, not to mention the *Guardian.* As is renowned folk singer Stan Crowther, who penned the mistaken identity plot of 'Welcome to Butlin's' (see Family Fortunes chapter) in a song some thirty years ago. Another actual event transformed into common legend is the one involving the children's radio host who lost his job after a moment of unintentional candour. At the end of the broadcast, he let slip, 'Goodnight little kids . . . We're off? Good. Well, that ought to hold the little bastards' and never worked again. Steve Avery of South Glamorgan wrote to tell us that the actual perpetrator was an early broadcaster called Uncle Dan, and the story is featured on a tape of radio cock-ups called *Pardon My Blooper.*

Still more stories have insidiously made their way into novels, sitcoms and movies. 'The parking incident' (featured in our Mean Machine chapter), for example, was recently used to great success in the film *Fried Green Tomatoes at the Whistle Stop Cafe*, but stories of this ilk have been doing the rounds for decades.

Some people will be only too keen to refute the truthfulness of some stories, notably the Disney Corporation, perhaps the commonest target of unsubstantiated and malicious rumours. The classic child kidnapping story (an aspect of paranoia dating back at least to Dark Ages Christian antisemitism) has apparently been the subject of an abortive *World in Action* investigation, amongst others. Mrs Robinson of Watford, concerned by the reports and close to cancelling her Disney holiday, actually rang the Foreign Office in London. 'Not true,' they assured her – and they wouldn't lie, they're the Government. (Both wink conspiratorially.)

really sorry, ***but we've got to stop there . . . (holds onion to eyes). Here's a big sack of money and a slap-up feed for your trouble.***

No problem, the pubs have opened now anyway.

antiques *roadshow*

Classic urban myths

Blow the dust off these cherished old classics, as we parade our well-worn chestnuts for inspection. These hoary old collectables have been handed down from generation to generation, and readers won't need Arthur Negus to tell them some of these heirlooms have been around since the Magna Carta. Add this treasure trove of fascinating pieces, honed by time, to your collection. They don't make 'em like this any more, madam.

saints *alive*

This old ex-pat in our area says he once worked at a rural undertakers' in Ireland that had been instructed by the Church to exhume the mortal remains of a nun who had recently been beatified. The bride of Christ had been buried in a convent graveyard back in the fifteenth century, and it was the undertaker's grisly task to dig down through the layers of coffins and bones in the consecrated soil until they came to the newly sanctified nun's casket. According to the church records, her coffin lay beneath twelve more recent interments.

The reluctant gravediggers began digging with gusto and a shovel. The first few coffins were in fairly good condition but, as they got deeper and deeper, the coffins became more rotten and the cadavers more crumbly. The undertakers began to worry, with good reason, that there might not be much of the recently promoted saint left to recover. The stench was unbearable, but they carried on digging by the light of a roaring brazier long into the night.

After what seemed like an age, the excavators found themselves raking through a putrid mix of earth, bone and rotten wood. Then one of their shovels hit something solid. They stooped down and cleared the rich soil from the wooden lid of the coffin – still in unbelievably good nick – and with some trepidation prised it off.

Inside lay the body of the saintly sister. Eerily, she was as immaculate and perfectly preserved as the day she'd died, five hundred years earlier.

the parking *incident*

The sister of a lady from down the road, beyond her salad days but still capable of freshness, had driven to the local out-of-town shopping park and was scouring the packed car park for spaces to leave her oversize, gas-guzzling metallic gold Mercedes. In one of those delicious moments, she spotted the last vacancy halfway down an aisle just before a beaten-up Beetle with two young women in it, which was rounding the corner at the far end, could stake their claim.

Swiftly establishing her precedence with a burst of speed and the wink of her indicator, the woman realised too late that her approach was all wrong. Her two young rivals in the VW hooted and waved their hands impatiently. But she was too close to the parking space in the narrow aisle and, with all the manoeuvrability of a super-tanker, had to crank the gears, blundering back and forth in order to achieve a position from where she could shoe-horn her vehicle into the space. This was too much for the fast-living youngsters. The multi-coloured Beetle revved up, streaked forward and sneaked into the parking space, missing the big Merc by millimetres and screeching to an audacious halt in the vacancy. One of the cocky young things wound down her window and sneered, 'That's what you can do when you can drive.'

The older woman showed no emotion, but slowly, deliberately, backed her car to the end of the aisle. Then she rammed her foot to the floor and, to the horror of the VW's occupants, hurtled straight down the lane, swerving at the last moment so she could slam full pelt into the Beetle, shunting it into cars in front and to the side. The two young women were speechless with shock and rage. The older woman's electric window glided slowly down.

'That's what you can do when you've got money,' she crowed, before cruising off.

> All right, all right, so you recognise that one from the film of the book *Fried Green Tomatoes at the Whistle Stop Cafe*, but several correspondents and relatives have assured us that versions of similar stories easily pre-date both book and film. This sort of literary delve into popular mythology is frequent – anyone who's seen the excellent movie *Hear My Song* will have recognised the scene where the cow is almost dragged down the well by a chain attached to a heavy object as an adaptation of the classic goat story we featured in our first book, *Healey & Glanvill's Urban Myths*. Some of these stories are as old as the hills – Benny and Jimmy.

the memory *man*

The brother of the secretary of our local philately society went on holiday to America in the 1980s and hit the heritage trail as soon as he arrived: Wild West ghost towns, War of Independence landmarks, Japanese car manufacturers . . . the lot.

One day the tour guide directed his charges to a native American reservation, where he recommended that the Limey visitors check out the legendary local 'memory man', a grey, gnarled old American Indian who made Keith Richards look like Tom Cruise. He could remember the most incredible everyday detail from the last sixty years, the guide assured them.

Having crossed the old cove's palm with the requisite silver, the tourist then posed the single question he was permitted to ask: 'What did you have for breakfast twenty-five years ago today?' he queried. 'Two eggs,' said the old chief, enigmatically. With no way to disprove this, the Brit withdrew, not particularly impressed.

Eight years later, on another jaunt across the Americas, the same tourist found himself driving through familiar territory – he was near the reservation with the amazing antique recollector. 'Ah hah,' he thought, 'Let's see how good his memory really is – I wonder if he'll remember *me*.'

Making his way to the old moth-eaten teepee, the visitor slipped inside and sat down unannounced opposite the ancient sage. Then he greeted him as he saw fit, beginning, 'How!'

'Scrambled,' muttered the old man, sucking serenely on his pipe.

the surgical *clipper*

During the heyday of punk rock in Devon – 1982 – a friend of a friend was working as a porter in a general hospital. Apart from a litany of unusual foreign bodies found in patients' various orifices, his favourite story concerned a punk rocker admitted one day for treatment for a broken thigh bone.

The snarling waif had safety pins through every protuberance, moribund-style make-up and a startling shock of green hair. When she was put under anaesthetic and disrobed for the bone-pinning and leg-plastering operation, the surgeon was not altogether surprised to see that the punky patient's pubic hair was dyed green too, and above it was tattooed the saucy legend: 'KEEP OFF THE GRASS'. Naturally, for hygiene reasons, this had to be removed, and was swiftly shaved off.

An hour later, operation satisfactorily completed, the young woman was returned to her ward, where she shortly regained consciousness. Studying the full-leg plaster for the first time, she was embarrassed to read the surgeon's ironic felt-tipped message: 'SORRY, I'M AFRAID WE HAD TO MOW THE LAWN'.

holy *orders*

A vicar near Tuckenhay in Devon was renowned for his thoughtful Sunday sermons, though not for the reasons he hoped. He considered himself the Rabbi Blue of the West Country; the few remaining members of his flock thought of him more as a rabid bore. His Sabbath lessons seemed interminable, but such was the power of his lungs, as well as the possible fierce recriminations (brimstone etc.), that not one of his flock had ever fallen asleep during his services.

One exceptionally hot summer's day, though, the believers filed into church as usual, and assumed their positions on pews. Sitting in some of the best seats in God's house were a farmworker and his young son, a plucky eight-year-old. The father had been at the village hotspot the night before, and it had been one of those nights where you ask the twinkle-eyed barman when he's closing and he booms, 'Tomorrow, zir!' So, hungover, but keen not to show it, the bloke was considering the option of matchsticks to keep his tired eyes open.

Meanwhile, the cleric began his Sunday pitch, beginning with a quiet preamble that had some parishioners leaning forward to catch his drift. Then he suddenly raised his voice to a crescendo to hammer home a point. The late-night drinker stirred, but was soon slipping Nod-ward again. The priest's parable was really hotting up now, his neck vivid purple as he lectured about personal morality, anomalies in the Exchange Rate Mechanism and the drawbacks of auto-erotic asphyxiation for the single man.

By this time, the 'ennui' factor was taking hold of his audience. Ladies waved fans, men shuffled, people coughed, and then – horror of horrors – a huge snarling snore broke out. It was if Beelzebub's own beany breath was in his midst, but the preacher continued as if nothing had happened. The subterranean snorting and wheezy whistling continued. The vicar raised his voice to temple-crumbling amplitude, but still the drunken snorer's noise competed for attention, and other parishioners were beginning to giggle.

Finally, the cleric broke off his sermon and hollered at the snoozing man's son, 'Will you wake your blasphemous father up immediately!'

The boy shook his head.

'Do as I say, wake him up right now, you cheeky young scamp!' bellowed the preacher.

'Why don't you,' scowled the boy at last. 'You put him to sleep!'

the dockyard *thief*

A neighbour who was a docker during the Second World War recalls the time a workmate had fallen under the suspicion of the harbour police (sometimes known as the 'river filth'). Every night at dusk, the burly fellow strolled up to the dock gate on his way home, pushing a wheelbarrow with a large grubby oil cloth draped rather dubiously over it.

This was a time of hardship and shortages, and it was feared that the bloke was half-inching some of the essential wartime supplies, which arrived daily at the port, to flog on the black market.

Every night the dock police stopped the docker at the gates and checked under the cloth for illicit goods. But the handcart was always found to be empty. Undaunted, the puzzled coppers continued with the inspection every night for weeks and weeks. But each time they lifted the cloth, the barrow was found to be bare, and the shifty docker resumed his journey home with a cheery wave.

Apparently, one enterprising young bobby, desperate to solve the case, eventually followed the docker home and watched him trundle up his back alley, open his yard gate and wheel in the barrow. When the suspect had gone indoors, the energetic PC scrambled over the backyard wall – and found 57 stolen wheelbarrows stacked up in the garden.

> Another version of that criminal classic is set at a North African border checkpoint where drugs and weapons trafficking is endemic. For years a guard watches a shifty man walk through the crossing in the morning and return in the evening on a bicycle. The guard always thoroughly searches for contraband, but never finds anything. On his retirement day, the curious checkpoint charlie privately asks the part-time cyclist to let him in on his secret – what is he smuggling, and how? 'Bicycles,' is the bloke's grinning reply.

the flat*mate*

A university student was staying over with her boyfriend and stopped off at her flat *en route* to pick up some smart togs for college the next day. It was late – in fact, she checked her watch and noted it was 11.48 p.m. Then she quietly turned her key in the lock and silently switched on the lights so as not to disturb her slumbering mate. A few seconds later she was rifling through her clothes and cursing her co-habitant for the irritating habit of borrowing her best clothes without asking.

So the young woman sneaked into her friend's room and, as delicately as she could, searched through the huge pile of clothing on top of a chair. Just as she located her smart accoutrements, the poor lass accidently set off a Polaroid camera and the flash exploded in the dark. Her friend let out a groan and the woman rushed out pronto.

Later that night, there was a loud rap on the boyfriend's door. It was the police. They confirmed that the student was the woman they sought and then gently broke the news that her flatmate had been violently murdered.

Then they produced a Polaroid exposure found at the scene. The young woman took one look and blanched. It was the last snap ever taken of her friend. There stood the flatmate, trussed up, her assailant's arms clamped round her, with a hand gagging her mouth, and, nearby, a clock. It was blinking out the time: 11.59.

the *stiff*

A wily old hospital porter liked nothing better than to scare the living daylights out of new workmates with nasty initiation rituals. One of his favourites was to put an amputated finger complete with gold ring between his own fingers and ask a gullible novice to help him remove his stuck ring. To the youngster's horror, the severed finger would come off with the ring, and the veteran prankster would laugh his socks off.

One day, though, the lads apparently decided to get their own back. They pulled out a vacant drawer in the morgue and one of the mischievous scamps stripped naked and lay inside like a stiff, intending to sit up, wailing in a ghastly fashion, and give the old porter the shock of his life when he opened the drawer. The others nipped off to find their quarry and set him up.

But after several minutes lying down on the slab, there was still no sign of the ageing porter, and the young lad was getting agitated. It was at that moment that the corpse next to him rolled over and moaned, 'Cold in 'ere, innit mate?'

> Again, a variation on a popular theme, always involving an initiation and a spell on the slab. Far preferable to a rather longer spell in a slab, as in this next old chestnut.

set in ***his ways***

An old war buddy of my grandad's used to work on the cement, at about the time the boys from the blackstuff were constructing the M1. He would barrow the stuff from the mixers to the workings or direct the flow from hoppers into the fabrications.

The contractors he worked for weren't such a bad bunch but the foremen always kept a beady eye out for malingerers or tea-leafs – back in those days many rogues were to be found working in the construction industry. All very different from today, of course.

During one winter they were building a bridge support for a motorway viaduct and the weather was atrocious. The buttress needed gallons of ready-mix and the blokes had been outside in the lashing sleet for what seemed like weeks.

One old fellow had been off-colour for a while, coughing and carrying on, but he was dedicated to the job and determined to stick it out for the shift (plus they'd dock his pay if he skived off early). The first layer of concrete was down in the morning and the gang were finishing the second, with the minimum of supervision, just before dinner break.

That afternoon the sick bloke didn't return for work, so his mates assumed he had toddled off home, but a few days later his whereabouts were still a mystery to his wife and kids. To those workmates who'd seen him nip off to another part of the site for a short nap, it was quite obvious where he was. The company could have demolished the support just to make sure, but you can't stand in the way of progress.

> Of course, we've all heard about numerous East End villains being forcibly entombed in the foundations of various motorway constructions. The final resting places of these pillars of underground society must be seen as prime examples of a rare cooperation, where hardened criminals have wholeheartedly supported a Government project.

torch*ed*

A member of Her Majesty's constabulary got more than he bargained for back in the days before motorcycles enjoyed the benefits of electric lights. In those far-off times, the intrepid biker's path would be lit with the aid of temperamental acetylene lamps – about as reliable as a mini cab service's 'Five minutes, mate'.

These notorious contraptions not only had to be lit with a match but were incredibly untrustworthy, spluttering out at the drop of a skid-lid, for no discernible reason. Not only that but they were the very devil to relight, and virtually guaranteed the rider badly burnt fingers.

So it stands to reason that motorcyclists generally rode around poorly illuminated. The police, even in those days, were hot on this flagrant disregard for the rules of the road and many a biker suffered the consequences of inadequate technology. (Cars were pelting around at speeds of up to 15 miles an hour, so it was in the rider's own interest to maintain safety measures.)

One winter's evening, a lone motorcyclist was wending his way home battened up against the sleet, when a police constable leapt into the road, arm outstretched. As usual the two-wheeler's lamp was extinguished. The bloke's heart sank – he had been collared by the same copper more than once in the past for this offence, and things looked grim. As the caped knight of the road strode smirking across the cobbles, the bloke trotted out his usual excuse, 'It's only just gone out, officer – honest.'

The old law defender shook his head. 'How many times have I heard that? Try pulling the other one, it's got bicycle clips on. This time you're for the high jump. Any fool can see this lamp's as cold as ice.'

So saying, he slapped his palm down hard on the lamp's casing. Sadly, he'd miscalculated and sustained severe third-degree burns to his favourite truncheon hand.

> I first heard that on my grandad's knee, dressed in short pants. I don't know why he didn't wear long trousers like other men, but there you are. To be honest we're not quite sure what the attraction of that story is or why people still tell it. I mean, what's so funny about a policeman getting his fingers burned?

highway ***to heaven***

An alderman from Tadcaster in Yorkshire, where all the best beer comes from (apart from Boddingtons and Courage, of course), knew a local parson who had encountered his fair share of adversity. Once the venerable old cleric was driving his brand new Austin Seven (we're talking about a while ago) through the summery dales when it spluttered and conked out.

The padre was distraught. He had a wedding to officiate in an hour. It was at the next village some miles away and now he'd foolishly run out of petrol. Then remembering that he'd passed a garage a short while back he clasped his hands together, praised the Lord and, gathering his cassock about him, set off at a pace.

Upon reaching the garage he enquired of the pump attendant whether there was a receptacle into which he might put a gallon or so to alleviate his predicament. The grease monkey shook his head glumly, then pointed to a scrap heap out the back and burbled, 'Mebbes yowl fand summat over yon, reverun'.'

The vicar scrambled about on the rubbish tip, but the only thing he could lay his hands on was a child's enamel potty. There was nothing else for it. He'd have to use that, unsuited to the task though it was. Filling the gusunder (goes under the baby, gedditt?) to the brim, he set off back to his stranded motor.

It was the middle of summer and the vicar began to build up quite a sweat, especially when he realised that the yellowy liquid was rapidly evaporating from his open receptacle. He reached the car with but a dribble left and was just pouring the dregs into the petrol tank when a gleaming Bentley purred up. A dowager in the back, all wrapped up in mink, saw the red-faced clergyman at his task.

'Oh parson,' she sighed, 'I wish I had your faith.'

trunk in *charge*

Some years ago, when zoos were cruel places where animals were actually treated worse than humans (unlike today's Health Service, where humans are treated worse then animals), a family on The Great British Holiday – rain, Kiss-Me-Quick hats, chips, amusements and guaranteed 24-hour tedium – set out for a West Country zoo.

Dad pulled up in the car park, and mum and the three kids piled out of the Mini and in through the entrance. Minutes later, the nippers were hanging off the chimps' cage, scratching their armpits and grunting (no unusual behaviour there, you might think). The parents were watching a keeper training a teenage Indian elephant to sit

on a big red stool, without much success. 'He'll sit on anything red except this bloody stool,' muttered the bloke, deciding to take the errant pachyderm for a stroll instead.

After a few hours complaining about the various nose-assailing whiffs from animals and the fact that the lions, polar bears, pandas and other interesting creatures are always off apparently sleeping noisily in their dens at the other end of the compound when you want to see them, the family called it a day.

Heading wearily out of the gates, the family were struck by a commotion in the car park. The keeper they'd seen earlier was shouting to his junior jumbo to get up, but the hefty beast was refusing to do so. As they rounded a few more parked cars, the tourists were horrified to witness the scene before them: the soppy elephant had mistaken their red Mini for one of its stools, and mistakenly plonked its considerable khyber on the small car's bonnet, cruelly crushing the poor little motor.

The car was almost a write-off, but the keeper promised a quick insurance settlement – the elephant was covered, fully comprehensive.

Hobbling back to the holiday flat in the twilight, the maltreated car was rattling and scraping and soon caught the attention of the police.

When the inquisitive officers saw the damage, they enquired as to its cause. The father earnestly explained the whole sorry tale. But to no avail. The two coppers looked at one another, then one leant forward: 'D'you want to persist with this ridiculous yarn, sir, or just come clean and blow into the breathalyser?'

dober*manned*

A smashing couple called Teh and Caz moved on to a new estate in one of Liverpool's outlying districts and immediately caused concern among the rest of the Toxteth farmers (Scousers who'd moved into the sticks to better themselves with a bit of garden). The reason for this was not their manner or anything they did, but the fact they brought with them their two adored and slavering hounds – vicious identical twin Dobermans – that were forever running through an oversize cat flap into the garden and irritating neighbours with their noisy, brutal playing.

But the owners soon settled in the area, and made many new friends. In particular, they hit it off with their next-door neighbour, and when after nearly a year in residence they asked if he would look after their dogs while they were away for a week, the neighbour readily agreed, despite his fear of the pets.

The first few days were uneventful. The neighbour put the dogs' food in a bowl and poked it through a gap under the garden fence, and both dogs would rush out through the cat flap to scoff it, greedily nuzzling each other out of the way.

But after three days, the helpful neighbour noticed something strange: when he pushed the edibles under the fence, only one of the sneering beasts came through the hatch. The next day, the same thing happened: just one of the deranged beasts emerged. The bloke began to wonder if the hound had bumped off its twin, or whether it was simply ill. A few days later, although he was terrified, the neighbour girded his loins and decided to investigate. He couldn't stand letting his new friends down.

So he gingerly climbed over the fence brandishing the door keys, and let himself into the house. The dogs were evidently upstairs, judging by the sound of their growling and sneering. Sneaking up the stairs so as not to provoke the dogs, the neighbour looked over the banister on the landing and was shocked at the scene in the bedroom.

For three days the two Dobermans, their faces screwed up in a hellish sneer, had apparently been terrorising a young would-be burglar, now a quivering wreck covered in blood and far from hygienic in the toilet department. The mad mutts had been working in shifts, taking it in turns to eat and then keep the burglar at bay.

> It's usually added that the intruder was so psychologically disturbed by his experience that he was never fit enough to stand trial.

the *mole*

A friend's accountant lives out in a swanky commuter village just beyond the M25. Every weekend the place is seething with city suits careering around the country lanes in their Range Rovers or sipping spritzers in the local pub.

One local yuppie used his Christmas bonus to purchase a huge mock-Tudor thatched villa on the new Prince Charles village-style development. His was the largest house on the estate and he fancied himself as the local squire, sporting the requisite tweeds and brandishing a knobbly walking stick. His pride and joy was the huge bowling green out front which he employed a recently retired old boy to manicure for a pittance.

But one day disaster struck. A mole, oblivious to the concept of trespass, left the lawn looking like the Somme on a bad day. The yuppie was mortified and demanded his gardener put paid to the disruptive creature immediately. 'I don't care how you do it, just make sure!' he screamed. The old boy was none too sharp but set about dispatching the subterranean troublemaker with a spade.

A few hours later the mud-spattered gardener feebly tapped on the back door. 'Oi've sorted that mole good an' praper,' he announced.

'What did you do – poison it, shoot it, trap it?' quizzed his employer.

'Noither, zir,' came the reply. 'Oi caught the bloighter, an' Oi buried 'im alive.'

call me *mother*

Our sister's friend and her new husband were enjoying a romantic soirée at a top-drawer restaurant. Staring mistily into each other's eyes, they noticed an elderly lady sitting alone and gazing in their direction.

They smiled back politely and the old dear made her way to their table. 'I'm sorry to trouble you,' she began, stifling a tear. 'But you look so like my daughter. She was killed last year and I do miss her terribly. I wonder if you'd do me an enormous favour?' The couple nodded compassionately. 'It would give me such a thrill if, just as I am leaving, you would say "Goodbye mum", and wave me off.'

'Certainly,' the couple replied. How could they possibly refuse? A few minutes later the old lady gathered her belongings and stood up to leave, and the two diners cheerily waved and said goodbye as 'mum' tottered out. Feeling good about themselves, the couple asked for their bill. But after checking and rechecking they called over the manager, demanding to have the massive total explained.

'That includes the charge for the lady's meal,' the manager revealed. 'She said her daughter would pay.'

madame rompy-*pompidou*

In the 1970s, relations between Britain and France – what with the Channel fishing wars and arguments over the Common Market, not to mention understandable offence taken at both the Queen and Edward Heath's appalling French accents – were at their lowest since Napoleon described us as 'shopkeepers' (what a short-arse Froggy bastard!)

Perhaps in an early recognition that our future destinies were closely entwined, all sorts of diplomatic missions were set up – Bernard Manning did a nationwide French tour, Charles Aznavour was allowed into the UK charts without a passport – but nothing apparently beat the arrival in Britain of the enigmatic Madame Pompidou, wife of the president of the day.

Things reportedly didn't go too well, especially as Madame P. insisted on applying her unfathomable accent to the Queen's English. Everything came to a head (in more ways than one) when the stately dame was introduced to a prudish old member of the British government at a big State banquet.

'It's such a huge pleasure to meet you, Madame,' suppurated the nob, as the assembled blue-blooded throng hung politely on her every word.

'I 'ope you 'ave a penis all your life,' Mme Pompidou was heard to pronounce, to the evident shock of her confidant, whose monocle fell into his Pimms.

'What can you mean, Madame?!' stuttered the abashed old buffer.

'You know,' explained the serenely smiling Frenchwoman, ''Appiness, joy . . .'ow you say – a good time . . .'

> That one's been attributed to virtually every one of France's *première dames* since Josephine.

welcome to *butlin's*

An acquaintance from Lancashire was enjoying her well-earned summer holiday, with smiling hubby at the wheel of the family Ford Zodiac cutting a swathe down to Clacton. The kids had only said 'Are we there yet?' a dozen or so times, the sun was shining and they had a fortnight in Butlin's to look forward to – what could be better? The journey had been a breeze and as they cruised towards the thronging camp with its inviting neon sign their hearts leapt.

It was perfect, everything a Wake's Week family could dream of: fairground, hairdressers, full English fry-up, late-night chippy, talent nights and cheap beer on-site and on tap. The moment they arrived a jolly Redcoat led them past row after row of happy holiday homes to their bijou prefab chalet with all mod cons; there was even a shower and bunk beds for the kids.

The chatty Redcoat handed over the key with a cheery wave and the kids pelted off to the amusements. At last the parents were alone.

'I'm off to use that shower to wash away the grime of that long drive,' the husband crooned, stepping out of his trousers with a saucy wink. 'Come and join me if you like . . .'

'I'll just pop out and get some provisions from that little shop we passed,' replied the wife. And she danced out of the door, swinging her shopping bag like a satchel.

A few minutes later, her carrier bulging, she skipped in through the open chalet door. Spotting her naked spouse towelling himself dry with his back to her, she lunged forward, grasped his wedding tackle and bellowed 'Welcome to Butlin's!' while nibbling his ear.

The bloke nearly died of fright – she'd got the wrong chalet and goosed a complete stranger.

When that one appeared in our regular column in the Weekend section of the Saturday *Guardian*, we received an interesting correspondence from Mr Stan Crowther which gives us a clue about the nature of 'mythologising'. Pleased to see his work established in the nation's folklore, he suggests that the Butlin's story derives from a folk song he wrote and performed over thirty years ago, called A Visit To Butlin's. From which, we hereby reproduce the final, cautionary verse:

'So come all married women, take a warning by me –
If you go off to Butlin's for a week by the sea,
Be sure you can recognise the man you have wed
Even when his shirt's right over his head.'

Excellent stuff.

straight down *the middle*

An Accrington couple had had an extremely acrimonious divorce. The case had trawled up both parties' dirty linen and exposed it to the public view. It wasn't a pretty sight.

After much deliberation the courts had decided that the only fair way of separating the warring couple's affairs was to split the house and all its contents 50:50 between them.

The husband was outraged. Convinced he was the wronged party, he followed the court's directions literally to the letter and divided everything – furniture, clothes, carpets, lampshades, the fish tank, the house itself and even the car – exactly in two.

With a chainsaw.

the royal *wee*

My boss and his mate out in Windsor were keen joggers who practised regularly and always promised themselves they'd enter the London Marathon next year, but somehow their training programme never quite peaked at the right time.

One day he was tramping the woods and lanes thereabouts alone for the usual stint, a three-mile jog then a marathon ten pints. Crunching through the fallen leaves in his trainers, he felt the call of nature and knew he wouldn't make it back home to use the facilities. So he checked the coast was clear and popped behind a tree to relieve himself.

He was just shaking the drips off when he heard an irritated woman's voice behind him, saying, 'Would you mind not doing that, young man?'

And lumme if it wasn't the Queen herself, taking her corgies for their constitutional.

She should think herself lucky he didn't turn round, standing to attention, really . . .

wish you *were here?*

Trouble abroad

Some charmers from over the fence in the Global Village. These postcards from the edge reveal a world where the grass may be greener but not as green as the travellers; they're out of their manor and out of their depth. A snapshot of the New World Disorder as frontiers tumble and trots around the globe become a way of life. It's a brave new world, but you've gotta be brave to brave it. Nowhere over there is safe . . . And remember – do forget your toothbrush.

pit *stop*

An ageing English colonial officer, serving in India at the turn of the nineteenth century, had the good fortune to employ one of the most expert cooks in the whole of Bombay.

And if he wasn't the most hygienic fellow in the world – his BO was as potent as *phang*, the local potato hooch – the colonel forgave him anything whenever he saw his delicious-looking dumplings. They were so round they were almost perfectly spherical.

Given the minimal kitchen facilities available, the Englishman considered his cook's balls near-miraculous. (We should point out here that, for once, no *double entendre* should be inferred from our language: we are talking doughballs here . . .)

In fact, the sad old bloke kept banging on about his chef's dumplings to anyone who'd listen, and as he was always keen to ingratiate himself with his superiors, he invited the local commissioner round for a mouthful one evening. His cook's dumplings were to be the centrepiece.

Come the evening, the chef surpassed himself. The dumplings were as perfectly round as ball-bearings, and the meal was a huge success.

'How the devil does he do it?' enquired the impressed commissioner, asking for more. Smugly (even though he'd never discovered the secret himself), the host suggested his guest go see for himself. So the commissioner poked his head through the beaded curtain into the kitchen – just in time to catch the cook rolling the last of the dumplings in his fetid armpit.

on the *right track*

During the years of prohibition – the pernicious killjoy scourge fashionable throughout America in the 1920s and 1930s – a team of railway engineers were trying to blaze a trail for the iron horse across Canada. They were running behind schedule largely because of the shirking labourers, a motley bunch who drank much harder than they worked.

The situation wasn't eased by the presence on-site of a huge vat of whisky in one of the supply wagons. Many were the times one of the temperate bosses would stumble across his employees leaning against the wagon with a soppy expression and breath you could light a barbecue with.

There was obviously no way they could just destroy or take away the whisky – it would endanger the whole project and labour relations weren't too hot anyway. So the bosses put their heads together and came up with a solution. One of them casually announced to the men that the vat had originally been found with a Chinaman's head preserved in it. News of this spread like wildfire throughout the rail gang. But the result wasn't what the management had hoped for.

The story had been invented to stop the men drinking so much, which worked. But nearly all the men checked themselves into hospital the next day, supposedly with excruciating pains in their stomachs, and more working days were lost on the railway than ever.

> Clearly of some vintage, that one, and related to the classic concerning the old colonial bloke's remains pickled in the barrel of rum found and unknowingly supped by workers in an old house. We featured that one in our first book of urban myths.

bridging ***the gulf***

An American GI was among the earliest soldiers sent over to Saudi by the oil-obsessed Western powers and UN to help put the original dictators back in control in Kuwait and depose Saddam Hussein. After months of stalemate and brinkmanship, war finally started, and our hero was one of the first to see combat – and very nasty it was too.

While out patrolling just inside the Iraqi border, the Yankee trooper and his pals spotted an enemy light artillery unit without being seen themselves. Quick as a flash, and in an impressively smooth manoeuvre, Uncle Sam's men surprised, overwhelmed and captured the entire platoon. Then they set about interrogating their captives – pleasantly, of course. It was at this stage that the young GI had the surprise of his life. For among the motley crew of supposed Saddamites, he found himself face to face with a very good friend of his from back home in Chicago.

japan 3 *east germany 1*

A tourist recently back from the trip of a lifetime to see the cherry blossom in Japan (no, nothing to do with shoe polish) heard tell of a number of bizarre incidents that seemed to reflect the world number one economic power's obsession with work rather than people.

One involved an abandoned car found in the Tokyo gridlock traffic. Apparently the other inscrutable drivers had shunted it around in the nose-to-tail snarl ups for three whole days without a driver at the wheel.

Soon after, there was another disaster. Apparently the rules of the road are so strictly adhered to that an impeccably law-abiding Japanese driver starved to death at a faulty set of traffic lights which had tragically become stuck on red.

Both those stories are reminiscent of the myth concerning the Japanese business commuter who sadly passed away on the Tokyo Circle Line and travelled round and round for three days before anyone even noticed. That could obviously never happen here, where everybody's so deeply concerned for their neighbour's welfare on the tube – unless there's only one spare seat left.

There's also a hint of similarity in the tale of an East German shopping party on a coach trip to Frankfurt, set free in a consumer paradise, who in their purchasing frenzy noticed one of their comrades on the coach was dead, but left him there for three days while they desperately completed their spending spree. What's worse for capitalism, he presumably hadn't bought a thing.

bearly *credible*

Two friends from Cleethorpes were on the European leg of their round-the-world trek. It had been an eventful time: they'd been punched in the Balkans and nearly strung up by the Urals – painful indeed.

And then one day they found themselves in the Tyrol, backpacking their way through rural Austria in a mist as thick as a whale omelette. Both friends were getting very tired and worried that they were lost in the wilds. The pea-souper meant there were no landmarks to be seen and night had closed in long ago. One traveller wanted to pitch the tent anywhere, but the more cautious fellow wanted to try to find the campsite they'd seen on their map.

Three hours of blind wandering through the thick forest, however, soon convinced both of them that they should bed down in the first suitable area they stumbled across. Pretty soon they found a low fence. Believing there might be some open land behind it, both lads scrambled over. The area was open enough, but boggy.

Exhausted, one of them dumped his stuff but the other walked on a little further and came across a wall. 'I'm just gonna climb this wall and see what's over there,' he shouted. 'It might be drier.' And he began to clamber up the stonework.

But his pal wasn't going to budge an inch. 'You can bloody well give me a hand putting this tent up first,' he bellowed back. At that the other trekker stopped his ascent and strolled wearily back to find his friend. As soon as the shelter was erected, both fell asleep like logs.

First thing in the morning, the less adventurous of the two went for a walk and found the wall his friend had discovered the night before. Interested to see what lay beyond, he scaled it.

By the time he reached the top, his companion was nearby too. Looking down from atop the obstacle, he tried to contain his fear.

'Good job we didn't camp over the wall last night,' he said, his voice quivering. 'It's a fifty-foot drop down to a pit full of hungry brown bears.'

dolomite ***triumph***

Last winter a couple of mates decided to get away from it all and splash out on an adventure holiday hiking in the beautiful Dolomite mountains of Northern Italy. They were both sickeningly rugged outdoor types bursting with health who thought nothing of running for a bus or climbing a steep flight of stairs after a heavy meal.

The lads were experienced mountaineers and prudently made sure they packed all the right gear – sturdy boots, crampons, cleats, distress flares and, most important of all, a good supply of lumberjack shirts. They weren't ones for taking unnecessary risks.

The first few days were fantastic. They set out on long exhilarating hikes through the craggy topography, scaled mountains and soaked up the breathtaking views.

One day towards the middle of their stay they were well off the beaten path trekking towards a small remote village they'd spotted on the map the night before. The terrain became rockier and rockier as the gradient increased.

Then, as they rounded a bluff it became clear that the isolated village they'd seen on the map was perched on top of a volcanic plug; a wall of solid rock.

Taking no risks, the climbers roped up and began inching slowly up the cliff face in text-book mountaineering style.

The lads were exhausted but flushed with achievement as they neared the summit, and paused to catch their breath. It was at that moment that a young woman from the village flounced past them on her way down, pushing a baby in a pram.

colour *code*

Our window cleaner met a bloke on holiday who'd gone to Portugal for his summer break the previous year. One day the bloke had got a bit lost and, remembering the old maxim 'If you want to know the way ask a policeman', approached an officer of the law.

As we all know, the British bobby is renowned the world over for his courteous behaviour. But the holidaymaker was bowled over when the Portuguese rozzer not only drove him to his destination and bought him a drink, but asked him if there was anything else he needed and gave him a conspiratorial wink.

Greatly impressed with Portuguese law and order, the chap set out a few days later and, spotting the attentive policeman on point duty, went over to thank him, only to be shrugged off and completely snubbed.

Apparently, the Portuguese Secret Service agents wear

a distinctive colour of shirt which the holidaymaker had innocently donned on the previous occasion.

taken *for a ride*

A friend of a very vague acquaintance drives a black cab and often hangs around outside Waterloo Station, hoping a rich American tourist will flag him down and ask to be taken to Edinburgh Castle.

One day his enthusiasm got the better of him when he spotted a couple of confused German holidaymakers who were staring at a rail map and waving their arms about.

'*Sprechen Sie deutsch*?' the bespectacled husband pleaded as the cabbie forced the ample couple into the rear seat and stowed away their luggage.

'Yer, course mate – I was in the war, weren't I? Where you goin' – hotel, is it? I tell you what, a bit of sightseeing first, eh?' Then the cabbie pulled out in front of an ambulance and was away.

The tourists hammered on the glass and remonstrated as the cabbie wheeled them round Big Ben, then the Palace. So he took them to Harrods, but they still didn't seem satisfied and kept jabbing their fingers at the map, red in the face and yammering things he didn't understand.

Outside Madame Tussauds the taxi driver had had just about enough ungrateful behaviour and pulled back the glass.

'Look mate, what's your problem? Top-drawer tour this, all the sights an' that.'

As it happened, one of the couples' fellow countryfolk happened to be passing and caught their heated drift as it floated out of the cab window. Offering himself as an interpreter, he listened intently to their grievance with a knowing scowl.

'You cheating English *Dummkopf*,' yelled the passerby. 'They only vanted to know where platform 15 was!'

turned out ***nasty again***

A drinking companion from sunny Croydon was on his honeymoon in Turkey. The weather had been fantastic but that was about the only thing that had. The compulsory Turkish massage had been bad enough and in Britain would have guaranteed the leering masseur a ten-year stretch for grievous bodily harm, sexual assault and attempted rape (that was what he did to the bloke – you should have seen what he tried on the wife). Then he had the cheek to demand money for the aforementioned offences, claiming it was healthy.

Next the bloke's stomach started playing up, which after two weeks of recycled meat-style kebabs wasn't really any surprise. The state of the facilities wasn't really any surprise either. Imagine toilets à la Turque (a glorified hole in the ground), the heat, the flies and worse, much worse, the embarrassment. These aren't conveniences, they're *in*conveniences.

One day the Croydonians were well away from the hotel, being badgered in a 'genuine' bazaar, when the bloke knew he had to 'go' and fast. The stall owner heard his stomach complaining and led him quickly to the back of the shop.

It was the worst convenience so far, just a couple of footprints and a hole in the ground, but the bloke was far too desperate to care and dropped his trousers and everything else just after.

Relieved, he made use of his pocket full of hotel napkins and, buckling his belt, pulled the chain. That was his big mistake. The entire contents of the local sewage system came swilling up around his feet and over his shoes before he could budge. He waded out of the cubicle with the flies hot on his heels.

Smiling weakly at his new bride, he slopped back pitifully to the hotel, his turn-ups full of turnout.

the *cod slot*

In the United States of America, the land of the free, cable TV has become an epidemic and as yet nobody seems to have found a cure. The Yanks seem happy enough to produce and watch hour after hour of unutterable garbage, which they then try to flog to the world's entertainments markets. Even worse, worldwide TV stations are stupid enough to buy the stuff which, let's face it, is only going to encourage them.

One such new cable TV channel in the deep south of the United States had been granted a licence and was working hard towards its launch date.

In the meantime, to test the reception of its signal, the station was broadcasting a live picture of a tropical fish tank instead of a customary test card. The fascinating interplay between the guppies, neon tetras, parrot fish and other gaily coloured occupants of this undulating aquatic world allowed all the usual tests for colour balance, focus, ghosting, etc. The image was perfect for the job.

Then the day came for the big launch, and the station began to broadcast, starting with a sample of its best programming: a soap about lusty stablehands. But for the next few weeks the switchboard was jammed with irate callers demanding the return of the fish tank they'd come to know and love.

> Apparently the same thing happened with radio station Virgin 1215 (or was it Classic FM?). Before proper programmes were broadcast, the station played the melodious sound of birdsong 24 hours a day as a test signal. When Richard Skinner *et al* eventually cranked up the *rrrooockk* music, thousands of listeners complained, saying they vastly preferred tweets to twits. (Sorry boss, but no one's immune from a dose of mythology.)

fax *going on?*

During the Cold War the US Embassy in Moscow was under constant bombardment. If it wasn't sonic waves being sent through by the goddamn Ruskie spies in nearby buildings and making the staff knock off sick with mysterious head and stomach complaints, it was the Soviets using long-range microphones to pick up the sound of typewriter keys (they could tell which letters went with which key noise).

But sometimes the staff inside only had themselves to blame. There was the time, for instance, when a spunky young administration assistant, in the job for only a few days, was given the simple task of shredding some top-secret documents indicating the whereabouts of all Nato's nuclear-equipped subs. Anxious to impress her exacting boss, she failed to tell anyone she had never used a shredder before, and carried on regardless. Locating the machine, she lay the confidential papers down where indicated and pressed a button at random. The documents began to be processed and a few minutes later all had passed through the machine.

But when she looked down to see what state the classified info would be in, she was alarmed to see that all the papers were intact. It was only when her boss came over that she discovered she'd been using the fax machine. Under heavy questioning, she indicated which button she had pressed: the last number redial, of all things. Sweating, her boss pushed it again, and the word Pravda appeared – she'd faxed top-secret documents to the enemy's organ of propaganda.

> That shaky story has so many variations Elgar could've composed it. Close relatives of it include clerical assistant . . . blah blah . . . secret documents . . . blah blah . . . shreds when should have faxed . . . blah blah blah.

an otter *tragedy*

A Londoner working as an observer for Friends of the Earth was in Alaska during the *Exxon Valdez* disaster, when a massive crude oil slick devastated the local wildlife. Many thousands of birds and animals were killed, but the fate of one otter summed up the whole catastrophe.

Rescued in a tiny fishing hamlet slicked from snout to claw, the young scamp won the hearts of everyone with its pitiful expression and amiable manner. Though there appeared little chance of recovery, the little fellow – dubbed Tarka – was swabbed with detergent, force-fed mashed fish and vitamins and nursed conscientiously. One night the sea cat's condition became critical, and rescue workers feared the worst, maintaining an all-night cage-side vigil. Hourly news bulletins kept the anxious villagers informed and prayers were said.

Come the morning and a miracle: Tarka was romping around, playing with a ball and scoffing all the food he could get his paws on. The locals were ecstatic and when the revitalised otter was returned to the wild the whole village packed the jetty in celebration, along with news crews and even the detested local mayor.

'Let's hope it was worth the $50,000 it cost to save this critter,' scowled the mayor to howls of abuse. Then Tarka was liberated and everyone cheered as he dived into the briny, popping his head up several metres away and even – or was it a trick of the light? – waving a paw in thanks. No matter, for seconds later a huge killer whale suddenly burst through the swell and gobbled Tarka up.

the mad *greek goat*

Some Australian friends recently came back from a jaunt in Greece and were full of tales of the cradle of civilisation's way of life. One incident while they were there concerned a goat and an outside lavatory.

This billy goat was certainly gruff, in fact it was lethal. And for some reason he had decided that a certain territory belonged to him and him alone and he would brook no trespassers. This tract was a small rocky outcrop on the cliffs high above the sea. Not a place for foolhardy behaviour and the last place you'd want to be butted by an irate billy charging at full steam.

Normally this wouldn't have been too much of a problem, but at the very tip of this dusty outcrop was the only

Western-style toilet on the island, with proper sit-down porcelain and a chain to flush it, just like home.

For this reason alone many tourists from more molly-coddled countries would risk life and limb and run the gauntlet of the goat. It was great fun for the locals and provided an excellent spectator sport for habitués of the café nearby.

Then one day tragedy struck. The goat was found dead with its horns jammed under the rim of the toilet. It had been unable to remove its head after drinking the water and had sadly drowned.

> Sorry, but it has to be said: what a way to go. No wonder the goat had been so protective of its drinking water. I mean, how would you like it if people treated your well with such disrespect?

bombay *cow*

The same friends also heard tell of a poor Russian fisherman who had nearly been ruined by a most peculiar accident.

Apparently the fisherman was plying his trade on a huge Russian lake, the Aral Sea (he was one of the few Russian fishermen during the Cold War not secretly trying to make whales extinct on the orders of the KGB to destroy Western morale).

This lake is bigger than most small European countries and is like an inland ocean, with tides, storms and pollution, and of course a huge variety of aquatic life to exploit.

One beautiful calm day out in the middle of the lake,

the waves gently lapping against the side of the boat, the fisherman was contentedly hauling in his writhing nets when a cow suddenly appeared in the sky from nowhere, smashing right through the middle of his boat and sinking it instantly.

The fisherman was distraught. His livelihood was ruined at one fell swoop of a Friesian. Who would believe such a thing? Certainly not the insurance company, that was for sure, he reasoned to himself as he clung on to a floating spar waiting to be picked up.

Back on dry land his suspicions were confirmed. The insurance company laughed out loud at his implausible excuse. It was the daftest story they'd ever heard. They sent the ex-boat owner away from their office with a flea in his ear and a squelch in his shoes. The poor man turned to drink for solace, his life in tatters.

This remarkable story became the talk of the Urals, and came to international attention. It was then that the embarrassed American embassy privately intervened in the man's life, surprisingly admitting full responsibility for the incident. They bought the delighted trawlerman a brand new state-of-the-art boat with all the trimmings.

Apparently what had happened was this: a huge USAF transport plane had been flying a relief mission in the area and one of the heifers on board had gone berserk, kicking a lieutenant and dribbling on an officer's trousers. In their apoplectic fury the flyboys decided the crazed beast had to go. So they opened the cargo hold and heaved the mad cow out into the wide blue yonder at 3000 feet.

hands across *the water*

A well-to-do young Cambridge University student took a year off to visit Australia and immediately looked up that side of his family deported in shame (probably for forming a trade union) some two centuries earlier.

They lived in humble circumstances in Melbourne, but when the posh Pom arrived, he was treated like royalty. So much so that he actually acted the part too: he stayed for six months, though he'd originally said it would be 'just a week or so', and during that entire period he never even offered to help out with the household chores. They took him to all the sights: off-roaded it through the bush, went to the opera, took him to the beach whenever he wanted – all for no gratitude whatsoever.

Naturally, the Oz family were intensely annoyed by this plummy relative's patronising manner and feet-under attitude, and when he announced the date he was leaving, it couldn't come soon enough for them. The saving grace was that when he came to depart, he suggested that the family might look him up and his rich widowed mother in their huge country seat when they visited later that year.

So the Aussies – mum, dad and two young kids – took up the offer and, when they arrived at Heathrow, they immediately rang the toff who'd stayed with them. His mother answered the phone and as soon as she ascertained who they were she crooned, 'You really must come up for tea'. This was alarming to say the least – they'd been expecting to be put up at least for a week after the hospitality they had extended to her obnoxious son.

However, they decided to travel to the mansion, deep in the Yorkshire dales, that very day. But the journey was a nightmare. The weather was horrid – wet and windy. The hire car was cramped and had taken a bit of a caning, and conked out three times on the journey north. Worse, their relatives' actual village wasn't on any map and they had to ask a dozen people in the locality before they got the right directions.

Finally, just before 11 p.m., they were bombing up the drive of their ancestral seat and were thrilled in anticipation of what they would discover about their forebears.

They knocked at the door, but no one seemed to be home – no lights were on. Then finally the twin-setted lady of the house creaked open the door. Telling them to leave their bags in the car for the moment, she led them by candlelight to a dim, dusty study with a real fire glowing feebly on one side, and explained how expensive electricity was in this day and age.

The mother disappeared and soon returned with a plate of ginger cake and a pot of tea and listened distractedly to their description of the journey with a soppy fixed smile.

Half an hour later, she stood up, clasped her hands together, said 'Well' and began walking towards the door. The family looked at each other – was she saying they should go and get their bags from the car now?

But then their worst fears were confirmed. The plummy Sheila simply thanked them for coming and, without ceremony, showed them through the door and out into the rain-drenched night.

> Let's face it, that one cuts both ways. There are as many tales of oikish Aussie Relatives From Hell as there are ones about poncey Pommies who abuse hospitality. Then there's the notion that the British don't wash (we do! *every* month!) or that Aussies' legs drag and that all the men are sexist goons. Honestly, anyone would think we didn't really like each other.

International

- Italian vineyard owners slaughter an old cow and bury it under each new vine planted to encourage fertility and improve the flavour of the produce
- In some suburbs of Dublin, there are traffic lights with green signals at the top
- Princess Anne was the only competitor who wasn't sex-tested at the 1976 Montreal Olympics
- A man who stole a car during the 1989 San Francisco earthquake was found crushed under a fallen section of motorway
- Because of their country's matriarchal Catholic society, one in seven Spanish men lose their virginity to a prostitute
- Gangs of vicious thugs in Nairobi collect penises as talismans
- Burkina Faso's national football squad once flew to play an important tie in Sierra Leone and forgot to take their kits. The opposition wouldn't loan them their spare strips, so they had to haggle for gear at a local market
- The United States government has a contingency plan to change the currency overnight in order to scupper the fortunes of drugs barons
- Zaire's national goalkeeper was so heavily weighed

down with various fetishes when his team played a crucial cup match that he wasn't able to dive

* At the top of every big mountain in the Himalayas, climbers always find a café full of people
* If you drop a coin from the top of the Eiffel Tower, it will go straight through anyone it hits on the street below
* In the early years of German reunification, hordes of 'wessies' would hire coaches and drive through the east, taking souvenir photos of the impoverished 'ossies'

animal *magic*

Beastly tales

This documentary of wildlife encounters shows Mother Nature in the raw. A grand safari of yarns, from pampered pets to the beasts of the field. (You'd have to be barking to believe them.) Specially for those who fancy a walk on the wild side, but mind where you step: something might be dogging your tracks . . .

taking *the mickey*

My mum's neighbour's son bought a male pup and was as proud as punch of the little blighter. It grew into a strapping mongrel that would hold its own in any scrap on the estate, so the bloke was even more proud of its enviable reputation among his friends.

But one thing about the dog was a source of ridicule: when it went for a leak, it wouldn't cock its leg like a male dog, it would crouch down like a female. Local people were remorseless in their whooping laughter whenever the dog performed its wimpy act.

Eventually the owner was driven to distraction and could stand it no more. So he took his dog to the vet and asked his confidential advice. The vet packed him straight off to a top animal physiologist who'd come across this problem many times before and suggested there was a simple solution. 'The best thing to do is be a role model when you're out walking. Demonstrate to him yourself what he should be doing.'

For three weeks the barracking from his neighbours was infinitely worse, seeing him out with his dog and pretending to urinate against trees and lampposts.

But three weeks later, the dog had stopped crouching to leave a splash. One evening, the vet happened to pass as the owner and his dog were out 'walkies'. The animal doctor enquired how things had gone. 'See for yourself,' said the bloke, proudly indicating his pooch. The dog was having a leak all right, but standing upright on its hind legs in front of a tree, its front paws on its groin, and attempting to whistle – just like its owner.

walk*ies!*

An elderly woman who used to be the doctor's receptionist at my uncle's surgery lived in a quiet part of Harrogate. In her comfortable retirement, the dotty woman – a widow – had found a furry companion with whom to share the autumn of her life. It was a gorgeous little poodle and she was devoted to it, cladding it in ribbons and other canine accoutrements.

The spoilt pooch went everywhere with its venerable owner, and was as pampered as Mrs Slocombe's pussy. She wouldn't let it out in wind or moderate sunshine, and at the first sign of rain or a sniffy-nosed dog, she would rush home to save her mutt from a cold or worse. When she was on heat, the poor bitch was locked inside for days.

But one day, as the sun was shining brightly and there wasn't a dog to be seen anywhere around, the myopic woman drove over to a nice park in her old Morris Minor. It had been raining for days and she'd promised her pet a good runaround.

After a lovely stroll round the municipal fields, the old dame was just returning to her car when a friend tapped her on the shoulder. They hadn't seen each other for years and there was a lot to catch up on, what with deaths to go over, infidelities to dissect, new hats to pour scorn on and so forth. The poor poodle got frustrated and began tugging on its lead. The woman was being pulled all over the place and the lead was getting under her feet, so she temporarily tied the leash to the back bumper of her car and continued her chinwag in peace. It was a toasty summer day, and she always heeded the RSPCA's advice about not leaving dogs in cars on hot days in case they dehydrated.

After a few minutes the poodle was getting very agitated, but for once the woman ignored her pride and joy. Then it began yelping loudly; oddly though, the whine seemed to drift away. Naturally concerned, the old dear broke off the chat to check things were OK. To her horror, she saw her beloved pooch being dragged along the tarmac by an accelerating car. The soppy dame had attached the leash to the wrong car's bumper.

horse *play*

Horses don't have much of a life when it comes down to it, especially the racing ones: from punter's fancy to steak pie in the snap of a fetlock. But there was one poor old nag whose fate was worse than Shergar's (far worse: the famous missing thoroughbred is apparently crunching carrots in Libya after a top-secret 'arms-for-bloodstock' deal).

The twelve-year-old horse, not the top racer in its Wiltshire stables, was lined up to race at a national hunt meeting a couple of hundred miles away. But its hard-hearted trainer had used up all his good boxes on mounts with a more realistic chance of success, so for the journey north it had to fit into a decrepit one-pony transporter salvaged from a haystack in a swampy part of the yard. The horse box looked like something a New Age traveller would keep his or her dog in rather than the conveyance for a classy hunk of horseflesh.

Warily, the horse staggered up the splintered gangplank and entered the dilapidated crate. It was awful: no windows, no space, no eating facilities, a decayed floor and the rancid smell of chicken wee – exactly like a student flat-share, in other words.

The sad old stallion was reassured by the callous trainer and locked in the dark as the Frontera towing it lurched off down the muddy lane.

If only the trainer had watched a little longer, he may have averted an utterly awful equine tragedy, for just a few hundred yards down the road the poor horse's hooves went through the rotten floor of the transporter. But despite the dreadful panicking whinny, the driver kept his heavy foot to the floor. By the time the transporter pulled to a halt, the nag's legs were sadly worn down to stumps.

Where would our Urban Myths books be without the regular set of canine savages? Here's a few doing the rounds that give the lie to the idea of 'man's best friend'. With fearsome friends like these, who needs enemas?

what *a choker*

An Eastbourne vet was called out to dispatch a Doberman pinscher that had been big trouble ever since it was a finger-nipping pup. It liked children, but only if it couldn't find anything else to eat.

With some trepidation, the animal doctor approached the home of the savage beast, but before he arrived he was met by the distressed old lady owner. She explained that the dog had grown so psychotic now, she didn't fancy the vet's chances of topping him without thick gloves and an Uzi.

Boldly, the bloke strode up to the house and found the baying pooch tied up by its choker chain collar to a post by the front door. As he approached, the deranged dog lurched forward to attack the vet. But the bloke stood his ground and the dog throttled to a halt some feet short, constricted by the choker. As the foaming dog gagged and the garrotte tightened, the vet had an idea. Why waste any drugs? Why risk a bite from its rabid jaws?

He simply stood just beyond the reach of his adversary, pulling faces, and allowed the dim-witted hound to choke itself to death.

off *guard*

An Aberdeen woman, disturbed by the spiralling crime wave, resolved to take serious steps and bought the most fearsome guard dog she could find – a huge, filthy old beast until recently gainfully employed at the local docks.

On the way home with her new charge, the woman was impressed by its constant growling and its ability to make people cross the road as it approached. When she got it home, she sat the dog down and told it 'This is your new home, you must protect it and make sure no one gets in.' The dog listened intently.

A few minutes later, the woman set off for the shops to get the provisions needed for dog maintenance: food, kennel and tartan dog jacket (XXX-large).

But when she got home and turned the key in the lock, the soppy old guard dog came bounding down the hall barking its head off, with the hair standing up on its neck. The woman was terrified – her malicious mutt was about to attack its owner – and turned on her heels, slamming the door behind her. She spent the next few hours talking through the letter box to the brutal beast, trying to pacify it and gain entrance. But to no avail. As night fell she made one last attempt to get into her home, but was beaten back by the huge mound of canine hatred.

Deeply ashamed, the woman had to track down the previous owner at the dockyard and ask him – as he smirked snidely – to call off the slavering hound.

the *eel*

The bloke who used to live next door, a wildlife documentary film-maker, was overjoyed to land a commission from the BBC for their upcoming *Eelwatch* series. The film was designed to unravel the mysteries of eel migration and in time-honoured fashion a number of the slinky creatures were fitted with radio transmitters. The film-maker then joined a crack team of scientists charting the eels' progress back to the Sargasso Sea.

The boffins and TV crew crowded into the back of a transit van packed with equipment, communicating in hushed and reverent tones, and anticipating the first blip to appear on the screen. They didn't have to wait long. The signal was a good strong one and remained so as they charted the eel's slither up the bank from the river and overland towards a large pond. This was revolutionary stuff – no one had dreamed that part of the eel's annual odyssey involved terrestrial travel. Then the signal altered course again and, curiously, the eel headed towards a large housing estate.

Desperate in their quest for knowledge the excited team set off in hot pursuit of the slippery explorer. The signal from the transmitter got stronger and closer, so boffins and crew continued on foot, following the blip frantically until it became clear that the eel had gone as far it was likely to go: the signal lead unerringly straight into a nearby fish and chip shop.

> Apparently electronic tagging is now commonplace at Scottish salmon farms and the fishery protection unit often switch on their receivers when they are passing through the local residen-

tial areas just for a laugh. Quite often the machines go haywire with the number of signals coming in. The Press reported recently that a man was caught with a large number of tags in his dustbin – and an even larger stomach. What we want to know is what have these fish done so wrong that they have to be tagged and kept behind electrified security fences? Where's the evidence? We say, 'Free The Trout Farm Three Million'.

fel*ines*

When a young couple from Cirencester got married, domestic bliss took some time to establish itself. The young man was a real sad sack who doted on his pet cat. When the couple moved in together, the dratted moggy came too. In fact, the cat received more attention than the new love in his life. He'd kiss it first when arriving home, brought it dead mice which the wife despised, and it even slept in the middle of the nuptial bed.

One day, the husband sat down to the evening meal and remarked on how well cooked the food was. At last, a genuine compliment!

'We really must have that again,' he smiled, licking his lips.

'I'm sorry,' said his wife, shaking her head, 'but I refuse to let you have another cat.'

underhand *undercarriage*

A Liverpudlian chancer who a friend once met in a pub was dead proud of his new dog, a young pedigree Rottweiler that he hoped to enter for shows. Until, that is, a neighbour pointed out that the hound appeared to be lacking in the gonad department. The Scouser examined his pet between the legs and was mortified to discover that the bag was as empty as a soggy old balloon.

Clearly this put paid to his hopes of dog show glory and the lucrative breeding fees that could be commanded by a top dog. So the owner contacted his vet and had spherical silicon implants (extra large) fitted in his Rott's scrotum. Now fully equipped, the noble beast was entered for every prestige dog show around the country.

For a couple of months this fantastic example of canine manhood won everything in sight, and breeders queued up to have their prize bitches serviced. But before the first of these profitable ventures was tied up, the prize dog had another show to enter.

Victory seemed to be a foregone conclusion until one of the judges started taking an inordinate interest in the Rottweiler's toilet area. As the adjudicator fondled the dog's undercarriage, disaster struck. The poor mutt's original testicles dropped, plopping into the judge's cupped hand, and all its owner's plans fell flat.

trousered *snake*

My mum used to work with an 'exotic dancer' whose speciality was the rhythmic manipulation of her 10-foot boa constrictor. Snakes, contrary to popular belief, are not slimy, nasty creatures. In fact they are thoughtful, sensitive beasts, and this one was gentle, affectionate and absolutely devoted to its mistress: it would writhe around her legs in pleasure when she came in the house. In return the woman would bring home treats like live mice and chicks for her serpenty pal to eat.

After a few years of professional success, the partnership was threatened by the arrival on the scene of a young man who took the dancer's fancy. At first the snake was OK about him. But one day, a few weeks later, the woman returned from a short shopping expedition and called out to her boyfriend. There was no reply. She called again and then began to search the house. At last she found her boyfriend: in the bathroom, blue in the face and with the snake wrapped around his neck and chest. She rushed over and rescued the love of her life, and immediately took the boa round to the vet to see what had made him do it.

The animal doctor examined it and concluded that the snake had been driven to attempted murder by a terrible, lovesick jealousy. The heartbroken slitherer is still undergoing therapy.

mounting ***rescue***

A friend in the media was a videotape editor for BBC Wales, working on a series of day-in-the-life documentaries. One featured the work of search and rescue dogs in Snowdonia. These dogs are very telegenic and everyone loves animals, so the crew were looking forward to putting together a tip-top pop doc in the finest tradition.

A ruggedly handsome hound was chosen as the lead, fitted with the ubiquitous radio transmitter and given a few screen tests. Just at that instant, as luck would have it, a desperate emergency call came through. It appeared that a lone climber was missing in the mountains and the mist was drawing in. 'Perfect,' thought the director. 'Animals, human interest, lots of weather, danger and a happy ending – it's got the lot.'

An excited Rex snuffled hard at an item of clothing from the missing man's hotel room, quartered the ground, raised his proud nose to the air and shot off like an Exocet. The 4×4 mobile mountain rescue jeep tracked him up the mountain and thundered along the nearest pot-holed track in the same direction. A breathless reporter illuminated the viewers with vividly drawn descriptions as he and the camera followed the hound's progress on a radar screen. Then the blip appeared to stop and begin to circle.

'Bingo. He's found him,' the reporter yelled confidently. 'He must be under an avalanche and the dog's digging him out.' The reporter then explained that the well-trained dog would stay with the victim until the rescue team arrived to lend assistance. The rescue and camera teams leapt from the Land Rover and cut across the rough terrain. Thrilling pictures were being fed back live from the Steadycam operator, and the director couldn't have been more pleased with this nail-biting material. Seconds later the breathless crew crested the hill, expecting to zoom in on the heroic wonderdog – and there he was, vigorously 'rescuing' a stray bitch.

red *or dead*

Some engaged friends of a woman at work were strolling through a leafy park in Glasgow, soaking up the early spring sunshine when something caught the woman's eye, and she gasped. For just up ahead of them was a red squirrel squashed flat on the path. There were precious few of these beautiful indigenous creatures left without this kind of tragedy. The couple dashed over to the animal and the woman, choking back the tears, stooped down to carry the motionless squirrel into the woods and at least afford it some final dignity in death.

But suddenly the prostrate squirrel's eyes flashed open fiendishly. Then the beast pounced, tore a large chunk out of the stunned woman's outstretched figure, and sprinted away up a tree.

The poor woman was still distraught as her beau bandaged a handkerchief round the wound and swiftly drove her to Casualty. The boyfriend comforted his love as best he could while they waited in the long queue. As her sobs subsided she got talking to a sweet old lady in the next seat.

After a few pleasantries the couple asked the woman why she was there – she looked as fit as a butcher's dog. 'Well,' the old dear began, raising a bandaged hand, 'I was walking through the park thus morning when I saw a poor wee red squirrel lying on the path . . .'

terrier*ised*

A friend of a friend was going abroad on holiday and, unable to take her beloved Yorkshire terrier with her, persuaded her mother to look after the little mite. The mother lived on the tenth floor of a block of flats and was determined to look after the Lilliputian beast as if he were her own – or even better – and settled down to re-read her daughter's exhaustive list of dos and don'ts.

The next day the mother decided to take the little fellow out for a good brisk walk, invited her friend from the flat above, and arranged to call for her when they were on their way. She fastened the dog's little Black Watch tartan coat, attached his extending lead, smelled and then popped the pooper scooper in her pocket, locked her front door and called the lift.

The doors opened with a comforting 'ding' and she pushed the button for the floor above. But as the doors closed she was mortified to realise that she was alone in the lift. The terrier had bolted but was still on the other end of his expanding lead. She desperately reeled out as much slack cord as possible while the lift headed skyward to the next floor.

It seemed to take an age for the doors to open. Shouting hysterically at her puzzled friend to keep the lift there the old dear thundered down the staircase to the floor below, assuming the poor Yorkie was pinned to the ceiling, throttled to death. But as luck would have it, he was rammed up against the top of the metal doors, wearing a very tight collar and a perplexed expression, but otherwise unharmed.

cat *eats dog*

A family in Durham entrusted their pampered pooch, a chihuahua, with friendly neighbours while they went to Lourdes (or was it Lords?) for a few days. The neighbours were happy to oblige, though they were slightly concerned how their huge rag-eared ginger tom might react – that immense cat was a horrendous scrapper.

On the first day, the couple let their petite charge out into the garden to exercise its tiny legs. A few minutes later, they began to wonder if things were a bit too quiet and slipped out to have a look.

To their horror, the monster moggy was lying on the lawn prancing around with the half-eaten and obviously dead toy dog in its paws. The neighbours acted quickly, retrieving the carcass from the cat's claws and inventing a suitable story to steer the blame away from their pet.

When the people next door returned from their jaunt, the neighbours caught them before they went inside and explained in hushed tones that their dog had suddenly developed an horrific illness. They'd rushed it straight to the vet, who advised them that there was no hope: the poor thing was in such pain the only thing to do was put it out of its misery.

The sorrowful dog owners thanked their friends for their kindness and sloped back to their house. But an hour later, the bloke next door was back, and not in such a charitable mood.

'Are you sure our little dog was put down at the vet?' he asked, sternly. The couple nodded sheepishly.

'I only ask because I found this on our back door step.' And he held up the bloody, half-chewed head of his cherished chihuahua.

dummy ***hunt***

Over in the newly democratised former Soviet Union many new capitalist enterprises are battling for supremacy. The route to the top is obviously through trade and what could be better than exchange with good old Uncle Sam, conqueror of Communism and guardian of world democracy (unless you happen to be Grenada, or Nicaragua, or anything to do with oil . . .)

One Russian businessman decided he'd steal a march on his competitors and arrange a prestigious bear hunt for his potential American trading partners to curry favour. America has murdered virtually all its own bears, so it's only fair we should let them clear up the last few elsewhere, too. Plus they don't care how much they pay to do it.

Risk management is top of the tree at Moscow MBA college these days and the wily Ruskie thought he'd completely remove the potential for failure from the hunt by purchasing an ancient toothless circus bear who loved people and couldn't even have given you a nasty suck if he'd tried. With every option covered the businessman started counting dollars in the bank; the 'canned hunt' couldn't fail to be a roaring success (without too much of the roaring).

The day of the hunt dawned. The affable old bruin was released into the woods and the excited American hunting party began stalking. After a couple of hours with their guns cocked they were closing in on the tired old panting animal. In fact they could see it with the naked eye, ambling along ahead in a clearing by the roadside.

Steeling themselves to dispatch the hirsute beast, the Yanks were astonished by an outlandish turn of events that wrecked their sport. A whistling peasant cycling to market happened to wobble round the corner, came face to face with the shaggy brute and fell off his velocipede.

Momentarily remembering his twenty years in the ring, the sprightly old bear leapt on the bicycle, wheeled around in a circle and pedalled off as fast as his paws would take him.

no-go *cat*

A friend's sister used to work up the road in the local vet's and knows a thing or two about animals – at least, I hope she does. She heard a tale about the world-famous Ragdoll cat. You know, the huge fluffy chocolate-box kitties that go all limp when you pick them up (a bit like some women I know – which brings back a painful experience) and always appear unruffled no matter what.

It seems these cats are all descended from one particular cute dozy furball in America that was sadly hit by an automobile while she was pregnant. Ever since the unfortunate accident she and her daughters and granddaughters have always given birth to kittens which are incredibly placid and don't know the meaning of pain.

total *re-coil*

This bloke I met at football is a well-respected police inspector serving Her Majesty in the 'Land of the Prince Bishops', County Durham. In the course of his duties he has come across many a novel form of security, one of which could spell the end of the road for the Alsatian.

A young woman nightclub entertainer of the exotic variety often performed a double act with a huge African python, which featured many tricks of breathtaking acrobatic prowess and stunning feats of flexibility.

Despite the snake's popularity, the woman was often called away on business to perform other aspects of her extensive repertoire, and display talents which did not require the sinuous reptile's presence.

Sometimes such trips could last a couple of days but, as large snakes only need to feed once a fortnight or so, the huge constrictor was happy enough to be left locked in the bathroom with a full tub so that it could have the odd drink and a regular swim for exercise. It spent most of its time curled up on the mat asleep, or 'resting' as actors like to style such activity.

One weekend while the contortionist was away performing the police received an alarmed call from the woman's neighbours. It appears an unsuspecting burglar had broken in through the bathroom window – it must have been dark at the time – and, to his horror, immediately came across the resident reptile. It took the poor house-breaker three days to calm down enough to be charged.

> That hothouse of urban mythology, Bush House, home of the staff of the BBC World Service, was the source of the next tall tale, which again proves the universality of some phobias. To Western Europeans the story shapes up like the Christmas turkey story featured in the cover of our '*Return of . . .*' book, where a bloke buys a large fresh turkey from a farm at Christmas and is savaged by it in the morning. But in Eastern Europe where, until recently, God was blackballed by the Trots (ouch!), the winter ritual wasn't relevant, and a new twist has been wrought on it. (See Media section for fruitier examples of Auntie's apocryphals.)

dressing *for dinner*

A Polish woman, short of a crust and on the breadline, was the toast of her family after at last scraping together enough cash to buy a chicken for the big Sunday dinner. It was the middle of winter and the faces of the under-nourished kids shone in the candlelight. Her husband licked his lips in anticipation as she lifted the old boiler out of the sack and rapidly set about plucking it. A pan of water and locally-gathered herbs was put on to boil up for a soup *hors d'oeuvre.*

All of a sudden, the family's slap-up hopes were dashed in the most shocking fashion. The poor woman had pretty much plucked the whole bird when, tugging the last few quills from what one presumes was a particularly sensitive area, the hen, obviously stunned rather than killed by the farmer, leapt from her hands squawking, feeling raw, sore, but very much alive, and began clucking round the poor family's kitchen. The woman was mortified; partly because her family looked like missing their long-awaited nosh, but mostly because she felt so guilty at defeathering the bird alive. They all agreed to liberate the bird, but the children were concerned it wouldn't last five minutes in the freezing cold without its downy insulation.

Thinking swiftly, the Polish matriarch asked her youngest child to hurry and find some baby clothes. Then while her husband held it still, she dressed the chicken in the 'hen-me-downs' from leg to breast (even a crocheted bonnet). Not exactly the dressing she'd planned for it in the oven, but . . .

Shortly afterwards the family gathered round as their mother took the fowl outside to the front of the house and tearfully set it free. The chicken appeared dazed at first and stood there in its babygrow and other clothes. Then it darted away, straight out into the nearby main road. As luck would have it, a motorist happened to be steaming round the bend and spotted the darting swaddling clothes. Convinced he was about to waste a toddler, the driver veered off the road at the last minute, storming through some bushes and coming to a halt embedded in the front wall of the poor woman who'd just liberated the chicken.

> So that's why the chicken crossed the road (groan). Another fowl story doing the rounds at the moment concerns one of our rarest and most beautiful birds.

caught *shorty*

An old dear who's a bingo partner of my gran had always had a hankering to see the Highlands of Scotland before she popped her clogs, and booked herself on a crumblies' coach tour of the glens.

As she never went anywhere without her faithful Yorkie, she popped him inside her souvenir shopping bag with his head sticking out – his usual mode of transport. The wee dog was fairly well behaved on the bus and was a big hit with the other old cronies who were forever feeding the little fellow titbits from their Tupperware.

They trundled around the sights of the Highlands for a couple of days – salmon farms, Highland dancing demonstrations, displays of heavy drinking and fighting, excursions to woollen shops and the like.

One day the tiny dog yapped as it did when it needed the use of a suitable bush. So the old lady followed the

usual routine, called the coach to a halt, set the little fellow down and turned a blind eye. Sadly a golden eagle hovering above kept *its* eye peeled. It spotted the tasty morsel, swooped down and carried the yapping pooch off in its talons.

the hare *of the dog*

Well before Covent Garden became the flagship tourist paradise it now is, thanks to market forces and private enterprise (er . . . no, actually: thanks to intelligent long-term planning by the GLC) it was home to a thriving fruit and vegetable market. These days it's again often packed with vegetables, usually staring for hours on end at the street performers who contribute so much to the fun-loving ambience at the heart of the capital.

Back when the area was a working market, one foggy

day in London Town about seven o'clock in the morning, a costermonger was sauntering through the central arcade when he heard his name as plain as day – 'Mark! Mark!' – and stopped dead in his tracks. He looked all round but couldn't see any porters or anyone else.

Then he heard it again: 'Mark! Mark!' It was clearly coming from a short distance up ahead, so he hurried along, rounded the corner and peered through the early morning mist to see who was trying to catch his attention. To his astonishment, just round the bend was a scraggy dog with a hare lip, baying 'Mark! Mark!'

Animals

- The USAF tests the strength of its warplanes by firing chickens at the fuselages from specially-made guns
- 'Canaries' on market stalls are more often than not sparrows dyed yellow
- Cockroaches prefer to live in televisions and ovens
- Creepy-crawlies congregate in the ends of bananas – that's why our ancestors taught us not to eat the tips
- Tigers don't attack people face on – wear a mask of 'the face of the living idiot' on the back of your head, and you'll be fine
- Chickens are easily mesmerised
- Hamsters have an unusually high tolerance to drugs because of their high metabolic rate, so vets dispatch them by impaling them between the shoulder blades with a large syringe
- If someone dies on church property. the legal responsibility of informing the relatives falls to the vicar. When some gypsies left a dead donkey in a field owned by the church, a Sussex priest took an ad out in the local paper 'notifying next of kin'
- Termites use their weird-looking mounds to communicate with extra-terrestials on Jupiter, co-ordinating an attack on earth

* A killer whale once provided the evidence to convict a murderer when it sicked up a human arm at a marine wildlife park

the mean *machine*

Out-of-order technology

The following mechanisms have a mind of their own. It's just a shame the operators haven't. According to this workshop manual of technophobia we're prisoners of progress, and consumer goods become consumer nasties at the flick of a switch. If necessity is the mother of invention, when it comes to technology it's just the mother of all baffles.

state *of shock*

It was rush hour in the City and all the London tubes were jammed solid. A middle-aged rum-pot who'd enjoyed an extended publisher's lunch bustled his way to the front of the platform. Luckily there was no train approaching, because the fogey jostled just a little too much. He missed his footing and tumbled on to the electrified track, receiving a dreadful shock that sounded like a thunder clap.

The megavolt charge knocked him unconscious, and rush-hour people were screaming and fainting at the horror of it all. The marvellous emergency services arrived swiftly and in no time the bloke was back on his feet, apparently none the worse for wear. Until, that is, a smiling tube worker gave the unfortunate fellow a friendly pat on the back – and both his arms, amputated and cauterised by the shock, fell on to the platform.

Now that would never happen in New York, but *this* would.

sue-*icide*

A depressed Big Apple dweller attempted to commit suicide by throwing himself in front of a subway train. But the eagle-eyed driver spotted the falling figure and slammed on the anchors.

The train screeched to a halt just in time, leaving the proto-lemming with two broken legs and a ruffled demeanour. Several passengers inside the carriages, surprised by the emergency stop, also suffered cuts, grazes and crumpled newspapers.

This being the formidably litigious US of A, the

attempted suicide sued the subway authority and driver for damages and for being robbed of the democratic right to rub oneself out. He took the action on behalf of himself and those passengers injured as a result of the driver's quick reactions.

Needless to say, he won his case.

open ***the box***

In Stevenage one evening, a woman whose phone was out of order strolled a few blocks from her home to use a public phone and have a chat with her twin sister. Just as she picked up the receiver, a flustered young man tapped on the window, making out he needed the phone urgently. The woman, smug at having got there first, snidely lined up all her 50p, 20p and 10p pieces on top of the box and turned her back with a smirk.

Ignoring her frosty attitude, the bloke opened the door and pleaded for the use of the phone as it really was an emergency. The huffy woman shrugged off his pleas and carried on discussing the weather with her sibling.

Finally, after ten minutes, the aggravated bloke could stand it no more. He yanked open the door, pulled the woman out, tossed her change on to the pavement and picked up the receiver, muttering obscenities as he did so. The woman wasn't that bothered but gave the rude man the flying Vs and a piece of her mind, then sloped back home. As she turned the corner of her road, the world fell out of her bottom: her home had been burned to the ground, and the young man had been trying to alert the emergency services.

We've said it before and we'll say it again: everyone knows the most dangerous part of a car is the nut behind the wheel . . .

motorway ***deliverance***

A middle-aged man from Kidderminster couldn't believe his luck when he was driving past Birmingham on the M5 and there was virtually no other traffic on the road – and no rozzers either. Not one to miss exploiting any opportunity in his company car, the bloke was toeing it through the tarmac bedlam that is the area's road system.

But as he was storming round the bend of a flyover, he lost control of his Sierra, which hit the wall, flipped over and came to rest in a horrifying smash on the hard shoulder. The car was clearly a write-off, but miraculously the driver emerged virtually unscathed and absolutely elated at his good fortune.

Just to be on the safe side he quickly hopped over the barrier to avoid any more danger. Unfortunately, on the other side of the barrier was a 30 foot drop to another dual carriageway below. The poor bloke plummeted down and landed in the fast lane, where sadly he was run over by a Post Office van.

both ***ends burning***

In many suburban areas around the world there persists the rumour of a car – normally a Cadillac or other monstrous phallic extension – that has been curiously customised by its owner so that it has a front grill, bonnet and headlights at both ends.

It's been reported everywhere from Sydney and Texas to Suffolk in England. This spooky, motorised version of Dr Doolittle's Pushmipullyu appears at twilight and leads to all sorts of trunk road turmoil and roadside mischief. You see, in the heat of the moment, drivers would misread which way the high-octane leviathan was thundering and take evasive action, frequently causing huge pile-ups, believing it was careering along on the wrong side of the road.

But (like the Cambridgeshire village freak who burned holes through frilly knickers with a blow-torch – while they were hanging out to dry, we hasten to add) no one apart from the immediate witness involved is ever able to attest to what actually happened. And it's all been hushed up.

testy ***time***

A shy woman from Northampton was taking her driving test for the first time early one morning and was extremely nervous, dropping the car keys and trapping her seat-belt, then her dress, in the door.

The examiner was polite but severe. He told her to listen to everything he said (her personal instructor had already primed her about that) and not to look at him, but most of all to do what she thought was correct in any given situation.

She started the test well, and after a remarkably painless snail's-pace three-point turn and reversing round the corner, hit the usually busy high road with increasing confidence. But as she was slowly driving along, she was aware that the examiner was very quiet. Surely this was all part of the act, she thought, and continued driving straight, awaiting his call for a left or right turn.

But when half an hour had passed, they were into open country, and there still hadn't been a peep out of the official, the woman became concerned. So, still mindful of his warnings at the beginning of the test, she took a sneaky glance at the examiner. To her astonishment, the bloke was in a deep sleep, jaws agape, and they were thirty miles away from the test centre before she could wake him.

another *testy time*

A young man (from the same town by the sound of it) was taking his test and bursting with enthusiasm at the prospect of passing it and buying a neat little Mini. He began very attentively and successfully until the examiner raised his clipboard slightly. The driver had heard about this sort of test of reactions, and interpreting this as the sign for an emergency stop, he slammed on the brakes.

To the lad's horror, his passenger had forgotten to clunk-click his belt and, taken completely by surprise, hurtled forward, cracked his head and splatted his nose against the windscreen, then flopped back bloody and unconscious. The distraught bloke immediately drove him to a hospital, then fled home in morose mood.

The very next day, he received official notice that he had failed his test for driving without due care and attention. Attached to the bureaucratic kiss-off was a note from the examiner himself. On it he explained that when he had raised the clipboard, he was only taking a pen from the side clip.

the *close shave*

A mate of a bloke who gets his hair cut at our barbers' is a mad keen Hull Kingston Rovers fan. He follows the rugby league team all over the country. Well, all over the north, anyway.

On this occasion Hull were playing in a final at Wembley and the bloke and three of his mates piled into his gleaming new company car and headed south on the Friday night. They booked a hotel for three nights to make a weekend of it and couldn't wait to hit the Smoke.

On arrival the bloke, concerned about the rampant car theft and joy-riding in the south-east that he'd seen on the news, searched around for some secure parking. As luck would have it, near the hotel was a large well-tended multi-storey car park, with round-the-clock supervision. He booked his car in and told the attendant he wouldn't be needing it until the Sunday. In that case, the attendant advised, he'd be safest to park it on the basement level away from prying eyes.

The match was a screamer. Hull trounced the opposition, the lads were walking on air and desperate to celebrate, but they didn't know London too well and decided to use the car to cruise around town.

But when they arrived at the car park the attendant was, to say the least, unwilling to show them to their car and insisted that they would have to wait until Sunday as they had originally intended. Smelling a rat, the blokes called the police who also met the same resistance, despite cautioning the fellow that his behaviour amounted to theft. The attendant protested that the car was booked in until the next day and he couldn't allow it to be moved. It was more than his job was worth.

They soon found out why when they arrived on the basement level. The car was parked where the driver had left it, but lit by tripod arc lamps, and with three men hard at work on it. The brand new engine was on the back of a pick-up and a clapped-out oil guzzler was being shoe-horned in as its replacement.

over *and out*

A car nut mate down in Brighton knew a bloke who had an amazing car, a Spitfire. Not a Triumph, you understand, but yer actual Spitfire – a 27-litre Second World War fighter plane's engine coaxed into an Avenger's chassis.

He called it 'The Beast' and had this smart horror-movie-style graphic paint job in two-tone, candy-flip metallic. He used to get out on the M23 and burn off Porsches, Ferraris and the like.

One day this bloke was in the outside lane alongside an uprated Ford Codswallop, a turbo-charged monster. Of course they got into a burn-up. The Ford in the outside lane was doing well over a ton when the bloke in The Beast let him have it and, foot on the floor, rocketed past him. He was going so fast that he took off at the next corner and crash-landed a few miles away on the A27. Just near Biggin Hill, as it happens.

> Back in the 1970s during the brief blooming of custom car fever, one bloke put a gleaming supercharged Spitfire engine in the back of a customised Co-Op milk float. Apparently you knew if you were in his round because the milk was still warm from the cow. And all your front

windows shattered when he went through the sound barrier on his way back to the depot.

safety *last*

Back in the 1970s, Jimmy Savile was clunk-clicking all over the nation's TV sets and the Government decided to act fast. Only a few years later the safety-belt law was ushered in to a media fanfare. Most people followed the Government's thinking on road safety and were happy to comply in order not to get caught by the police and heavily fined. Up in Tadcaster, a friend of my girlfriend's mum always scrupulously obeyed the letter of the law and took to wearing her safety belt on all occasions.

Then one sunny Yorkshire day (yes, they do 'appen) the woman set off for a little shopping up in Weatherby via the A1. The traffic was quite heavy for a weekday and the greasy road was packed with careering lorries. Her car had only just reached 50 m.p.h. when an articulated lorry ahead of her jack-knifed and the poor woman ploughed into a metal-wrenching multiple pile-up. Sadly, she'd forgotten to wear her seat-belt and was thrown bodily through the windscreen on to the bonnet.

When she came to she was lying on a stretcher with a concerned police officer crouched beside her. Noticing she was now *compos mentis* the constable asked the woman if she was OK and whether she'd been wearing a safety-belt. The stunned woman, shocked at the callous officer's apparent lack of concern for her condition, glumly admitted that she must have forgotten to belt up.

'Well, madam, in this instance you're very lucky you didn't,' replied the officer. Then he indicated the tangled wreckage of her car. To her horror it became all too clear what the constable meant. For ripping straight up through the driver's seat was a huge shard of viciously jagged metal.

a relative *disaster*

A friend in the legal profession claims to know a family man from Halifax who was out visiting the folks. He and his wife were proud parents doing the rounds with the new baby, driving along at a sensible speed in the inside lane of the M62. The happy couple were chatting about this and that, with their pride and joy fast asleep in the carrycot on the back seat.

Suddenly a stone shot up from the wheels of a heavy lorry ahead and shattered the windscreen. Fighting with the wheel, the bloke brought the car to rest safely on the hard shoulder and whirled round, heart in mouth, to check the little one was unharmed by the frightening missile.

He was relieved to see the pebble caught harmlessly in the blankets of the carrycot, and turned back to his wife, who was seemingly in a state of shock. But when the bloke looked closer, it was clear she was dead: she had been dispatched instantly when the speeding stone shot clean through her skull.

pull the *other one*

Some years back, a widowed friend of my mum from the local historical society in Ramsbottom decided to fritter away some of her deceased husband's hard-earned cash and splash out on a lovely pale green Morris Minor to visit the grandchildren. There was only one problem: she couldn't drive. So she duly invested a little more of her lump sum in some lessons and passed with flying colours at the fifth time of asking.

Normally Morris Minors are the most reliable cars on the road, but she reckoned hers must have been a real Friday car. Not only was it impossible to start in summer, but the car drank petrol like there was no tomorrow and kangarooed everywhere, leaving acrid clouds of thick white smoke in its wake.

What with the fuel bills and taking it to the garage the whole time, it really seemed like her runaround was giving her the runaround. The oddest thing of all was that the garage could never find anything wrong with the vehicle.

One day, when the car had been in for the umpteenth time that month, a wily mechanic who was determined to find her driving at fault, asked the old lady to take him for a spin round the houses to see if he could spot anything unusual. Happy to oblige, the sprightly old blue rinse hopped into the driver's seat, carefully put on her safety belt, then pulled out the choke knob as far as it would go and hung her handbag on it . . . solving the mystery once and for all.

> Another favourite mechanic's yarn concerns a woman who keeps complaining of an infuriating rattle in her motor. But, as usual, all garage tests prove fruitless. Eventually, one of the mechanics visits her unawares at home and discovers that she had been keeping loose change in her glove compartment, but removing the money before letting the grease monkeys loose on her car because she doesn't trust them.

unearned *interest*

A bloke who went to Milton Keynes University knew this snotty mate who left with a Double First in computer studies. Everyone expected him to walk into a top job in the City but instead he just seemed to drift around doing nothing much. Strangely, though, he was never short of money. In fact he seemed to have cash to burn. Then suddenly, to everyone's surprise, he landed a top job at a well-known high street bank.

It seems he'd formulated a method of hacking into the automatic cash dispensers and extracting large quantities of cash without affecting his balance. The bank never caught on, but the bloke's honest nature got the better of him and he demonstrated his technique to the manager.

Straight down the cells for a long stretch you might think, but not a bit of it. They were so impressed with his abilities that rather than inform the authorities they immediately made him head of computer security.

> Two points to be made about that one. First, as most people know more about the private fantasies of the royal family than they do about computers, the classic epilogue to any story involving bits, bytes and balls ups has to be: 'and it was all hushed up'. This allows us to think we're being excluded from the conspiracy and gives the story a Big Brother overtone. Secondly, how many times have you heard of some 'whizz kid straight out of college' who makes millions either a) transferring money from the bank accounts of rich Arab students or b) hacking into programmes on big companies' payroll com-

puters to cream off a few pence every time any transaction is made?

hidden *extras*

A friend of a friend's hubby knew a bargain when he saw one, and he was looking at one right now. He had been scouring the papers for a runaround for his little woman but to date anything decent had cost more than he could afford. But, as he'd always reckoned, the car auctions had come up trumps. There it was, a nifty little hatchback, not too many miles on the clock, full MOT and a car alarm sticker to boot. It had even taken a magnet on every part of the bodywork except the windows.

Only one dodgy point: apparently it had been in a nasty smash. But you'd never know that to look at it. Couldn't get better value for love nor money and he'd tried both on more than one occasion.

A scratch of the nose, a tug of the ear and it was his. Cash on the nail and home to the missus. His wife was chuffed to pieces with her present and strapped hubby in for a spin out to the nearby countryside, stopping on the way at one of humanity's new cathedrals – an out-of-town shopping centre.

They were just nearing the top of one of those tummy-churning hills when the wife was dazzled by the warm glow of the golden evening sun. She pulled down the sun visor on her side, and an eyeball and a severed finger dropped out into her lap.

damaged *goods*

An electronics firm near Swindon – the Silicon Valley of the UK – was doing well and hoping to break into the big time. They decided to ditch their local supplier of components (chucking a few more people on the scrapheap into the bargain) and trawl around for cheaper providers abroad.

They came across a Korean supplier that priced their materials at a far more competitive rate than others and were said to be keen as mustard. But being of the stiff upper lip disposition and having swallowed all the wartime propaganda about Orientals, the managing director made his parts buyer attach a note to their order form suggesting that a component failure ratio of 1:100 (i.e. one dodgy bit of kit per hundred) was acceptable and nothing more.

In due course the consignment arrived from Taegu, and for the most part it was excellent material. But there had obviously been some confusion. Included in the package was a letter from the export manager saying, 'I have not come across the practice of failure rates before but, as requested, I include these with the order.'

Inside, as well as the five fully functioning parts, were five faulty ones, wrapped separately and clearly marked.

quite *a climax*

A health and safety consultant heard about a firm in the same line of business who were commissioned to make a video pinpointing the do and don'ts of modern forklift truck driving.

After some initial research they elected to shoot the film in a busy factory that had a large loading area beetling with

forklifts, right next to the canal. When approached the firm were only too willing to cooperate. They were proud of their safety record and made only one condition, insisting that the film would stress in no uncertain terms that none of their employees had ever been involved in any forklift accident of any kind.

The script was written and passed by the management. They were particularly impressed at the climactic catastrophe, featuring a loopy forklift driver and a fateful brush with the canal. The scene featured a stunt driver careering around the compound with a full pallet, then leaping from the machine just before it tumbled into the murky depths of the polluted water.

The day of filming dawned and the first few takes went swimmingly. With the bulk of the drama in the can, the excited crew set up for the climax. They checked again that every precaution had been taken. A crane and professional diver were on stand-by to retrieve the unlucky forklift. Just a few final tweaks and the stuntman climbed into the hot seat.

The cameras rolled and to everyone's delight the scene went like a dream: the forklift driver from hell hurtled around the yard breaking every rule in the book, skidded towards the canal and only just escaped by the skin of his teeth, the stand-in driver leaping free as the plummeting vehicle plunged over the quayside.

Swiftly dispatched with a crane hook to hoist the forklift back on to dry land, the diver disappeared from sight. The crew were still slapping the stuntman on the back and praising his screencraft when the frogman's head popped out of the waterway.

'Which one do you want?' he spluttered 'There's three down here already.'

> Forklift trucks are notoriously tricky to handle. One of the authors once personally demolished one of those retail skyscrapers made of cola cans while attempting a complicated reverse triple salko manoeuvre – not entirely on purpose, it must be said – and spent the rest of the day restacking the fizzing time-bombs in shame.

fuzzy *logic*

Isn't technology fantastic these days? A few years ago you had to lug around a bagload of lens filters, flashes and the like just to take a half-decent snapshot. Nowadays, of course, they've invented those new fangled idiot-proof cameras that anyone, even a complete novice can aim, point and crash-bang-wallop what a picture.

A friend of my auntie's from the biscuit factory went off on holiday with her mates to Torremolinos. They had a wild old time: sun, sea, sand and sangria and the men. Ay caramba!

She'd taken her brand new all-singing, all-dancing fuzzy logic autofocus camera to record the jaunt in glorious Technicolour. When she returned home, tired and sunburnt, she sent the photos off for developing. One morning a few days later there was a plop on the mat, so she kicked the cat off the sofa and settled down with a cuppa to relive the high spots of the vacation.

She couldn't wait as she fumbled with the envelope. It would be all there: Tracy topless on a high-speed inflatable banana, Sheryl doing the lambada with the chalet rep, and dreamy Darren from Leeds, who promised to keep in touch.

But horror of horrors! When she finally ripped the cellophane open, all she found were 36 identical pictures featuring a hillock of dusty pink soil.

In floods of tears she penned a letter of complaint to the developers and demanded compensation. What had happened to *her* pictures: they'd obviously been mixed up with those of a geology student or something.

But a few days later she received a disappointing missive from the developers politely explaining that she'd been holding the camera slightly, ahem, off kilter, and looking into the view finder the wrong way round. She'd actually taken 36 snapshots of her own left ear.

> Many things that seem to fall off the backs of lorries are available for sale in local hostelries and luckily, despite their unorthodox way of arriving on the open market, few of these items seem to bear the scars of their judicious plummet.

dishy *goings on*

A bloke who lives round the corner from the hairdressers' got his hands on a satellite dish that surely had been made available by cutting out the middle man, as it was purchased for cash and no VAT was offered or asked for. Being a bit of a home handyman, the bloke reckoned he'd soon have the thing up and running. Indeed he soon had it up, but getting it running was a taller order. With no instruction book to guide him, the amateur electrician made the best fist of the wiring he could and sat back to watch the big Monday night match.

But it was useless. He couldn't make out a thing on the screen and not even the sound seemed to be tuned in properly. So the bodger slunk off over the pub across the road as usual and got a lager in.

Just before the match started there was a raucous cheer. Somehow the landlord had picked up what looked like one of those steamy foreign adult channels. It was a bit fuzzy but before they switched over to the big match all the regulars were happy enough to leer at the sight of a hazy naked couple passionately making love.

Before every big match for the next few weeks the same thing happened: a snatch of adult skin flick then over to the blokes' real passion – football.

Then one particularly limpid night, atmospheric conditions must have been just perfect for transmission and the pub's monitors were crystal clear.

Looking up from his pint, the bloke nearly gagged on his pork scratchings as it suddenly dawned just why the romping couple on the big screen seemed so familiar: there, as plain as day, were his wife and their frisky next-door neighbour making love on the couch across the road.

He'd made such a hash of the satellite wiring that his dish was transmitting instead of receiving. His TV set had reversed polarity and was acting as a bizarre form of camera lens.

a *late surge*

A politician's life can be fraught with peril, especially during a general election, when many Honourable Members are forced out on to the streets to meet the people they most fear, the public. If pressing the flesh of rancid pensioners and kissing babies of suspect hygiene was not bad enough, add to this the indignity of travelling on public transport in order to appear a man or woman of the people.

At the last election John ***** (fill in the name according to political bias), was travelling up to Birmingham to rally the flagging troops. The train had been carefully selected to appear a spontaneous choice for the media rat pack and was full of InterCity business commuters. The politician toured the train swapping pleasantries and staging numerous photocalls, such as enjoying a BR sandwich and pretending to be a ticket collector – all with predictably hilarious results (as they say in *Radio Times*).

After half an hour or so the hearty first class InterCity gut-buster breakfast and prune juice chaser he'd consumed in haste that morning began to distract his attention and he signalled to his minders he was off for a strain on the train.

The Member had just finished his waste disposal when the 125 thundered into a tunnel. By a quirk of fate, another 125 was passing in the opposite direction and the violent force of the back-thrust pressure forced the contents of the toilet bowl shooting up and out, spattering his ankle-high trousers to the waist band with waste.

The politician was distraught. The Press corps were waiting outside and he'd ruined his best Armani. Rinsing the sodden strides before the next station and opening the door a crack he whispered to one of the spin doctors to fetch him a spare pair of rabble-rousers. They weren't perfect, but they'd have to do.

Thinking he'd got away with the fiasco, the next day the furious public servant opened the paper to find his electioneering outfit described as a well-cut steel grey double-breasted jacket and contrasting beige crimplene flares. Not quite the figure he'd intended to cut but more suitable than the possible Chelsea strip, perhaps.

> It's obviously unlikely that the victim was John Major. As all *Guardian* readers know – thanks to Steve Bell – he wears his underpants on the outside to avoid such calamities.
>
> Needless to say, engineering changes have now been made to all Railtrack tunnels and this kind of thing could never happen again. The biggest health hazard now is catching something from that slimy, streaky white matter that lurks on tops of sinks. Or soap, as BR call it.

more than *a bit flushed*

Sweden has an admirable record in all areas of health and safety. But only recently a very unpleasant incident drew attention to one blot on the social landscape, the train toilet.

As you would expect, Swedish trains are the height of technological sophistication. The well-designed, state-of-the-art public service runs smoothly on well-laid tracks, is clean and efficient, and of course always on time.

The railway's safety record appeared impeccable until an alleged incident with a vacuum flushing toilet, an appliance common on many of Scandinavia's iron horses. The toilets are now completely safe having been redesigned, but formerly the vacuum button was positioned on the waste pipe behind the seat. The button was later moved and can now only be pressed when the toilet seat in the down position. According to a couple from Vallingby near Stockholm, this redesign was forced upon the railways by a bizarre incident that took place at Östersund.

A Brunhilde-type woman of more than ample proportions needed to use the train convenience and plonked herself down hard on the porcelain, with the toilet seat in the upright position, creating an airtight seal. During her ministrations, she accidently nudged the vacuum button. This activated the sucking action, and the poor woman lost some her generous bottom round the S-bend. Mercifully this condition was only temporary, but it took a quick-witted cabin steward armed with a warm spoon to release her.

It's not known whether Diana Ross's 'Inside out'
is still one of the poor woman's favourite records.

However, in the hapless world of urban mythology, she's far from alone in her misfortune. And as this next selection proves, it's often a case of not reading the instructions properly . . .

pique *charge*

An elderly widow wrote to her telephone company to make a fierce complaint. When the customer services officer had deciphered her letter, he worked out that she had a very unusual problem.

The woman was receiving complaints from her relatives that she never answered the phone when they rang her. Furthermore, the woman didn't hear the telephone ring when they called. When the telephone did ring, it was always preceded by three loud barks from her dog in the yard. But when she picked up the receiver, there was no one on the line. 'How,' she wrote, 'does my Spot know when the phone's going to ring, when you don't even put my calls through?'

An investigator was sent round and began by checking the woman's hearing, muttering under his breath. Each time, the woman shouted 'I heard that,' so it was clearly no fault of hers.

The inspector continued his check by examining the telephone cable in the yard. But before he could get close to the wiring, he had to pacify the woman's excitable pooch, who was secured to the post carrying the cable by a chain.

Once he'd befriended the dog and examined the phone cable, the mystery was solved. The dog's chain was wrapped around the post and had worn through the plastic casing of the telephone cable chafing the core which carries a small electric current to operate the phone system and earthing it before the charge reached the phone. Each time someone rang the old lady, therefore, her dog received a dose of juice in the neck, which would understandably make it bark loudly.

On the third call, the cumulative voltage was enough to loosen the poor mutt's bladder. The results would eventually complete a short circuit between telephone cable and telephone, making the phone ring mysteriously for hours.

The woman was overjoyed to have the problem solved, and her dog even more so. 'How can I ever repay you?' she chirruped.

'No charge,' chuckled the BT man.

wash ***day blues***

A sobbing man phoned the complaints department of a large store to protest that his brand-new washing machine had gone berserk and wrecked his kitchen. His was a sorry tale spluttered out between sobs.

It seemed that the very first time he loaded the washer with laundry, it had gone into a violent mechanical frenzy, smashing his worktop in two as it cannoned up and down, before hammering across the tiles to demolish a run of cupboards. Then the motorised monster savaged the fridge so badly that the door ended up permanently jammed shut.

The astonished customer relations manager could hardly believe his ears. The type of washing machine in question was one of the most popular and reliable brands. How could such a thing have happened? Astronomical compensation figures swirled before his eyes as he breathlessly implored the customer to explain exactly how this bizarre and disturbing incident came about.

The fastidious customer had carefully followed the installation instructions. He naturally started at number one which read 'Remove all packaging'. This, he confessed, had been quite a struggle. The first bit had seemed simple enough: two layers of cardboard, then bubble wrap, followed by tape, plastic wedges and a few metal plates.

'But then came the tricky part,' said the householder indignantly. 'I had to resort to a hammer and chisel to remove that huge lump of concrete underneath.'

the appliance ***of science***

The consumer complaints department of a notable electrical retail store received an irate call from a distraught woman claiming that her recently purchased vacuum cleaner had exploded and demolished her kitchen.

The customer services manager tried her best to placate the tearful caller, explaining that she'd never before heard of such an occurrence. Personally, she found it difficult to believe such an incident was possible. She had been in the electrical business long enough to know that most nasty accidents with household appliances (especially vacuum cleaners) involved single men or Tory MPs. The caller reasserted the validity of her claim and explained the chain of events leading to the catastrophe.

She'd been cleaning the kitchen when a mouse shot out from under the skirting boards. Quick as a flash the woman aimed her nozzle and sucked the poor creature thudding into the dust bag. That was that, or so she thought until

she switched off the appliance, when she heard the ensnared rodent scrabbling about in a desperate bid for freedom.

The woman was mortified but again inspiration came in a flash. She turned on a gas ring, positioned the vacuum hose over the source and subjected the household pest to a severe gassing.

But when she switched off the vacuum cleaner the mouse was still defying her, scratching feebly. It obviously needed more gas. So she flicked the switch again. It must have caused a tiny spark and . . .

the shock *of the new*

The grandad of a bloke from up the road was badly electrocuted by a newly purchased carpet cleaner and he phoned the retailer to complain. The poor old chap had had a narrow squeak and was now recovering in hospital.

The complaints department took the call very seriously, but on checking the name, make and serial number in question they were astonished to find the machine wasn't electrically operated – it was, in fact, a carpet sweeper; all shake and no vac.

The perplexed customer services manager decided he had to see the appliance for himself and immediately arranged a site visit to the scene of the accident.

When he arrived at the customer's house he was shown to the fateful machine, made a few discreet enquiries, and the mystery was solved.

The barmy buyer had been furious at not finding any power cord supplied with the cleaning machine, so he took it upon himself to find a frayed length of electrical flex and attach it to three random screws on the sweeper's casing. Then, with his grandad poised for action in the middle of the carpet, he cheerfully told the old man he could wave goodbye to his dustpan and brush forever, and pushed the plug into the mains.

Scientific

- Colouring the rim of a compact disc, or freezing it, improves the sound quality (except those by Phil Collins)
- Record shops play everything faster to make it sound more exciting
- Arsenal's games at Highbury are so incredibly tedious that at one stage during a particularly bad match, the big screen began showing a film. (On another occasion, it screened Open University programmes)
- New shopping malls puff different smells through their air conditioning to make you feel good and spend more money
- Radar sterilises sailors
- Bored air traffic controllers see how close they can make planes fly without causing a crash
- A US university once lost lucrative research work for a huge agribusiness multi-national by wiping a file on its mainframe the professors thought was a student joke – it was called 'rat-penis-data'
- 40 per cent of automobile accidents occur in car parks
- New programmes in all software packages make a note of consumer habits of users and send them back to manufacturers
- Wrap your phone cards in cling film to recharge them

the *bill*

Law enforcement lore

It's easy to detect from these brief case studies from off the back of a lorry that the villains are often the victims. Learn your lesson and don't get on the wrong side of the Old Bill, or it'll be you on a charge and paying. If you're called to serve at the bar, make sure it's a pub: and if you're up before the beak, pray they mean Ian Rush. Proof, anyway, that we can string sentences together . . .

flying *carpets*

A friend living and working as a beach bum-cum-lifeguard in picturesque Adelaide (the only place to live in Australia if you want to avoid the six-pack lifestyle) was told by his friend living across the road that he'd be away in England sponging off his rich relatives for a few weeks. The neighbour further explained that he was having decorators in during the first week, but asked that his strapping pal keep his eyes peeled for any odd shenanigans at his pad.

The first week passed without incident, and the decorators had packed up and long since departed when the eagle-eyed neighbour happened to catch sight of two fellows in his cobber's driveway packing rolled-up carpets into their beaten-up DIY-mobile – you know, one of those Toytown delivery vans.

Adrenalin pumping as if he was thrusting through the waves to save a damsel in distress, the good neighbour apprehended the dubious pair with his most macho 'Oi!' Taken aback at first, the two blokes explained the situation: the owner had booked in his Persians for a steam-clean while he was away. The friendly neighbour was not only convinced by this but also spotted a way to recompense his vigilance. His own pad's deep-shag piles were suffering from bachelor fatigue and badly in need of a shampoo and set, so he negotiated with the lads to have the expense secretly added to his neighbour's bill.

The carpet cleaners loaded his mats into their van and phutted off down the road with a cheery wave. Needless to say, neither of the neighbours ever saw their carpets again.

Part of this next one appeared in our first

anthology of apocryphals, *Healey and Glanvill's Urban Myths*, and the story appears to be an amalgam of many different 'tricks of the trade' yarns. But it's worth recounting in its own right.

old *bag*

A middle-aged, well-to-do woman from Surrey was doing her Christmas shopping in Croydon (lovely shops, smashing people).

After five increasingly frantic hours deciding what to buy for maiden aunts and teenage nephews at a difficult age (aren't they the worst?), she'd bought the last present – the usual polyester socks with extra static cling for hubby – and set off, feet throbbing like a weightlifter's neck, in pursuit of a well-deserved cuppa in a department store café.

Minutes later, the pot of tea swiftly imbibed, the parcelled-up dame hobbled off to the toilets, found a vacant trap and sat down with relief, presents piled on her lap.

But as she was going with the flow, the woman suddenly spotted a scrawny hand sneak under the cubicle partition. She was so loaded up that, before she could take evasive action, the hand made off with her handbag. By the time she'd got herself together and opened the door, the sneak thief had scarpered.

Disconsolately, the old dame sought out Security and reported the loss of everything: cards, cheque book, Conservative Club sweepstake ticket, Neighbourhood Watch sticker and cash.

She didn't really hold out much hope for any of her possessions being recovered, especially so close to Christmas when money's tight, so it was even more of a pleasant

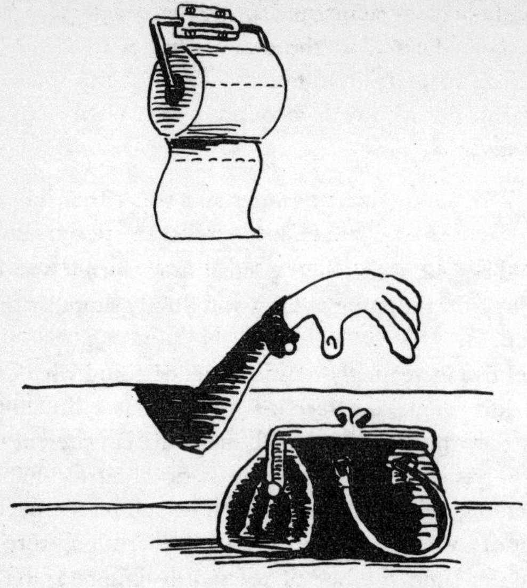

surprise when the department store rang her later that day. They said they had found her bag intact, and that if she came down straight away, she could take it home with her.

Elated at the forthcoming reunion, she dropped everything and hurried to the store. But when she arrived at the appropriate department, the assistant had no idea what the old dear was talking about. In fact, the young lady denied all knowledge of any phone call being made from the store. She recommended the gentlewoman return the next day when the earlier shift would be back on.

The poor disappointed shopper turned on her heels and sloped off to the comfort of home. Except that when she opened her front door with her spare key, it suddenly dawned on her that it was the handbag snatcher who'd duped her on the telephone. During her absence, the house had been stripped of its entire contents.

radio *daze*

New York is the citiest of cities and you either love it or loathe it; either way, you have to respect the resourcefulness and spunk of its inhabitants. Take the case of a friend from Scunthorpe who moved out to Manhattan to work as a social worker. His job took him to some of the roughest parts of town – Hell's Kitchen, the Bronx, the Stretford End – and he would invariably take his car, a little Honda, with him. And every so often, the dinky motor would be broken into, side window smashed, car stereo half-inched, and speakers wrenched from the doors.

Having lost three sound systems in this way, the honest bloke decided not to bother with the in-car vibes anymore. But mindful of the inquisitiveness of the local youth, he fashioned a sign reading, in vivid red, 'NO CAR STEREO', and stuck it on the inside of the passenger window.

Thus fortified, he set off on a visit as usual, parking in the housing precinct of one of his clients. An hour later, he emerged from the apartment and strolled over to his wheels, but was dismayed to see that, despite the sign, someone had still smashed in the windows.

The sign was still there, though, lying on the passenger seat. Picking it up, even the disgruntled bloke had to laugh when he saw it: next to 'NO CAR STEREO', the cheeky intruder had scrawled 'JUST CHECKING'.

the good *samaritan*

A young shop assistant who lived down the road from a friend saw that a sweet elderly lady was struggling to carry a laden shopping bag to her car and valiantly came to her aid. He was quite surprised that at first she seemed reluctant to allow him to help, but he put it down to the pride of people of her generation and how frightened some are these days. And soon she was thanking him profusely.

Over a period of seven months, the assistant helped her out every time he saw her. Then one day, just after he'd left the elderly woman at her motor, another young man accosted her. The shop assistant leapt to her defence, fists flying, and the woman scuttled off. But the assailant pleaded his innocence and tried to calm the shop worker down.

The bloke was a store detective and revealed that for the last seven months the nice old lady had been systematically shoplifting from the store – and that he, the charitable shop assistant, was to be charged as an accomplice.

disguise *no good*

A teenager from Wallsend – a close-knit community – entered a local Post Office during a quiet period, determined to hold the place up. He walked up to the counter brandishing an air gun and tapped on the glass, demanding that all the money be put in a bag and passed over to him.

One of the staff recognised him and addressed him by name. 'What d'you think you're doing, bonny lad? I know you, and your mam,' she said, more out of pity than terror.

The young man looked a little rattled, but reacted swiftly in impressive fashion.

'It's not me, it's someone else,' he stammered, before scarpering away empty-handed.

court *out (1)*

A young man charged with minor thieving offences was up before the magistrate, a nasty, hanging's-too-good-for– 'em merchant. The plaintiff 's sorry underprivileged life-story unfolded before the court, and the poor wretch stood in the dock, solemnly chewing gum and with his hands in his pockets.

The unsympathetic magistrate was irritated by his demeanour and interrupted the inexperienced defence brief to issue a stern warning. 'Tell your client to cease masticating at once!' she bellowed.

The shocked lawyer stopped, composed herself and leaned over to her client. 'Take your hands out of your pockets,' she advised.

court *out (2)*

A barrister representing the husband in a divorce settlement had been brought in at the last minute and wasn't too *au fait* with the case, so as soon as he arrived in court he asked the defendant to fill in his financial details on a sheet of paper so he could show them to the district judge.

This was swiftly done and returned just as they entered the chamber. The barrister quickly read the completed form with a little dismay. On the 'income' column, the bloke had filled in what he earned from his part-time work, added income support and tallied it at the bottom – it really was a pittance. Perhaps understandably, he had scribbled next to the column 'F. ALL'.

Proceedings began and, as expected, the stuffy judge suggested that to save time they could skip the cross-examination and complete the formalities on paper. The barrister, recognising that the use of the vernacular might scupper his chances, demurred, saying it would be just as quick to take oral evidence.

The judge didn't want to hear that, and requested that he be able to see the means statement of the husband.

The barrister stalled. 'Well, er . . .'

'You do have the completed statement, do you not?'

'Yes.'

'Well, then, I should like you to present it to the court.'

'We would rather not,' continued the defence brief, 'as it includes a colloquialism that may prejudice my client's case.'

'What sort of colloquialism?' queried the judge.

'I'd really rather not say.'

'Come come,' said the judge. 'We're all broad-minded people. Pipe up! What does it say?'

'Er, well . . . it says "F. ALL", sir.'

' "F. ALL"?'

'It's an expletive, m'lud.'

'Yes, yes, but what does it mean?'

The barrister hesitated a moment, before gathering himself and thundering, 'It means "fuck all", your honour.'

At which point the wife's solicitor leaned forward and, in a stage whisper, declared, ' "Family Allowance", you idiot.'

it's a *fair pot*

My uncle's friend, stuck in a dead-end job, was determined to better himself with a grand new career, but decided instead to become a police officer. His training went smoothly, and his first post took him to Manchester.

After a few weeks working on traffic control, he began to notice a pattern in the cars that were stopped by the officers: they seemed particularly keen to stop red cars and then black ones. One day he asked what they were playing at.

'Snooker,' came the reply.

The rookie was nonplussed.

'You see, we stop a red car – that's one point – and then we can go for a colour. There aren't many pink cars, but lots of black ones, so we go for them next. That's seven points.' And so on, and so on.

This was apparently going on in every force in the country. At least, that's what they told the new boy – and he's never bought a red car since.

motorway *madness*

The M57 traffic police received a number of calls from extremely distressed motorists and set out to apprehend a maniac driver who had being putting the willies up his fellow motorway users. After a long chase they pulled a bloke over who'd been hammering down the outside lane at 100 m.p.h., ignoring the traffic, looking backwards out of his side window with a hideous grimace on his face and terrifying other motorists.

It turned out that the fiend was actually keeping his eyes dutifully on the road, and had a mask with 'the face of the

living idiot' strapped to the back of his head to scare the pants off other road users. Regrettably this particular form of errant behaviour is not against the law and the police were forced to let the crackpot driver off, scot free (except for a speeding ticket).

trifle ***eyeful***

A friend from Bingley in Yorkshire knew an old copper who'd had an unpleasant experience. He'd been showing the ropes to a raw recruit fresh out of training school when the squad car had been called out to an accident on the M62.

They were the first to arrive at the scene and it was a nasty one. A van had been involved in a high-speed pile up on its way to a kids' party and was appallingly smashed up.

The young PC helped to extricate the driver from the front of the wreckage while his more experienced colleague went round to check the back.

The old stager wrenched open the mangled back door to be confronted by a mass of pulped matter. Even his stomach churned a little, and he decided to spare his young partner the gruesome sight on his first day. So the pallid older man tottered back round the front, clutching his midriff.

'Don't look in the back,' he croaked. 'Whoever it was is a goner for sure. Must've died instantly.'

It was only when the ambulance arrived and ascertained that the vehicle involved was a catering van loaded with cakes and puddings for a children's party that the mistake was spotted. Sadly the doleful old PC hasn't been able to face trifle ever since.

a dead *halt*

An acquaintance of a country doctor from East Sussex had a crony with a very peculiar monicker, to wit Dr Ezekiel De'ath, and was being driven home by this gentleman on one dark rainy winter's night. Suddenly a bobby on the beat stepped out into the beam of the headlights, arm raised in the routine fashion.

'Excuse me, sir,' intoned the constable, 'could I see your licence?'

'Certainly, officer,' replied the driver.

'Ah,' said the copper, clocking the name, Dr De'ath. 'I'm so glad I stopped you, sir. We've been trying to keep you off the road for years.'

crimebotch *uk*

The owner of a sub-Post Office in Surrey was approached one day by researchers from the BBC's *Crimewatch UK* advising him that they would shortly be filming some dramatic robbery reconstruction scenes at a bank up the road in his small town, and that he shouldn't be unduly worried about what he saw.

On the allotted day, the film crew arrived and set everything up, and the jobbing actors were trying their hardest to sound tough as old boots – none too convincingly, it must be said – as they put their make-up on.

Filming began and crowds gathered to watch the spectacle – nothing had ever happened like this in the town before – and the town square looked like a Chinese fire drill. The preliminary scenes in the can, the crew took a lunchtime break and all trotted off to the pub for some liquid nosebag.

During this period, the postmaster, who'd been kept informed of the television crew's progress by customers, was approached by another BBC researcher. The shell-suited young man explained that the bank involved in the original raid wouldn't look good enough on the telly, so he wondered if the postmaster would mind if they filmed a few short scenes inside his shop. The owner readily agreed.

A few minutes later two actors, balaclava-ed and tooled up to look like gunmen, burst through the door, pointed their Uzis at the postmaster, threatened him and demanded he hand over all the cash. Grinning and commenting that they'd arrived a little hastier than he'd expected – he regretted he hadn't had time to tidy up – the postmaster continued to make small talk as he gathered and bagged up the morning's takings, and handed the loot over to the thespian felons. The rogue pair turned on their heels and fled as quickly as they'd arrived, not even leaving the receipt he'd asked for.

Ten minutes later, the three men with cameras, leads and microphones came into the Post Office and asked where the power points were, followed by the director. The postmaster asked him why they needed power now – surely they'd acted out the scene just now?

The crew looked sheepish, and the director went pale.

'Not again,' he moaned. 'All our actors are still boozing it up at the bar. I'm sorry to tell you those were genuine robbers. And this is the second time in this series that someone's done that to us.'

a long ***stretch***

A friend of a bloke I know was in the dock for disorderly behaviour and, as a precaution against attempted suicide, all likely instruments – including the defendant's belt – had been removed when he was in the cell.

But during the hearing in front of the magistrates when the police made suggestions which he vehemently disagreed with, naturally the prisoner remonstrated, waving his hands – which had previously been employed holding up his baggy trousers – angrily in the air. And, just as naturally (gravity being what it is), the bloke's trousers suddenly slipped down around his ankles, to reveal that he had also been relieved of his underpants.

Eyebrows were raised among the female magistrates, who seemed persuaded by the defendant's impressive display, and he was immediately discharged.

over-***friendly***

A Welsh bloke was had up in court for various charges of indecency. The liberal-minded beak was reading out the various incidents and inviting comment, including possible mitigating circumstances, regarding each one in turn.

Among the alleged charges were importuning in public toilets and public indecency in a private cinema. After each episode was read out, the defendant didn't speak, but coughed loudly and waved his hands.

By the third charge, the judge began to feel that the miscreant wasn't getting a fair crack of the judicial whip, and offered something to ease the bloke's throat (if not his conscience): 'Would you like to suck a Fisherman's Friend?'

The bloke looked aghast. 'Don't you think I'm in enough trouble already?'

The law

- Chunnel police forces on either side have invented their own secret language so they can easily communicate to catch villains
- Because of an ancient by-law in Ross-on-Wye, an Englishman can't be prosecuted if he shoots a Welshman with a bow and arrow
- Every now and then police radio to each other the whereabouts of UFOs, then pounce on the public who turn up for illegally listening to police frequencies
- A thief who stole a car for a bank raid did the 'job' and found that his getaway vehicle had itself been taken for a ride
- Driving barefoot is illegal
- A man who interleaved hundreds of his own paying-in slips with those on his bank's counter got away with £13,000
- An incompetent burglar was disturbed and had one of his legs shot off, but still managed to cycle away
- John Dillinger, the notorious gangster, had a huge member. It is pickled and preserved at the Smithsonian Insitute
- A man was arrested in Indonesia for selling students 'magic pencils' that duped the computers marking their exams

* The following are apparently new EC laws:

- All British fishermen, no matter how burly, must wear hairnets
- Our Queen is to be banished from all postage stamps and currency
- Wurst of all, the sausage is to be standardised across the EC in line with the Germans': long, thick, and covered in leather

surgical *spirit*

Medicine balls

Life behind the mask can be a gas and this clinical casebook proves that the Hippocratic Oath's not the only swearing that medics indulge in. Under the quack, or under a bus – it's difficult to tell which is the more deadly. Trust hospitals to stitch you up . . . the fund starts here.

tijuana *'flu*

A young, free and single Surrey man was on the holiday of a lifetime in Mexico, thoroughly enjoying himself in the pursuit of melanin enhancement and local talent. His only problem was a streaming nose that developed after a few days, but he was prone to hay fever and the arid Gulf breeze had clearly done its worst, so he wasn't unduly concerned and kept the Kleenex handy.

One night, he found himself in the company of a dusky maiden at the bar of a romantic nightclub, and was trying his best to impress. His opening lines worked a treat, and she was bowled over by the fantastic stories of success and adventure he related (all about himself, of course). His banter was quality, and things were progressing nicely.

Then he proposed a toast to their 'fortuitous meeting' and took a hefty swig of his cocktail. The brown-eyed Mexican damsel's mouth dropped wide open in horror. She stared wide-eyed at him, blanched chalk white and careered off, hand over mouth, into the night.

The bloke was mortified. What could have shocked her so? He felt his face – nothing amiss – and his tie was straight. He resolved to leave and try his luck elsewhere. Looking in the Martini mirror behind the bar to check his appearance, he lifted his glass to down the dregs. As he did so, he spotted with rising panic two browny-yellow and slimy slug-like parasites slip out of each nostril and dip their feelers into his margarita, and then slither their way up again when he jerked back his head in horror.

hand *out*

A lady of Kent was travelling home by train from the Smoke on one of those ancient rattlers – more laughing stock than rolling stock – on a hot summer's afternoon. She was alone in the carriage apart from a sombre young man wrapped up in his reading matter – a selection of Edgar Allen Poe's ghost stories.

Absent-mindedly, in the heat and relaxed atmosphere, the young woman set about removing her false hand (did I forget to mention it? Well, see, she had this artificial hand, and . . .), and casually set it down on the seat, where for a few seconds it lolled around in bizarre fashion. The bookish bloke happened to catch sight of it over the top of his scary tome, and instantly turned as pale as marble. Then he jumped up, yanked the communication cord and, without waiting for the train to stop, disappeared with a scream through the carriage door, and hared off down the track.

Picking up the book from the floor, the woman soon realised why he'd reacted so strangely: the book was open halfway through Poe's spine-chilling tale 'The Hand'.

hard to *swallow*

A classified ad salesman, working for a large regional newspaper in Yorkshire, was renowned and despised for his machismo and stories of the purest bullshine. One Friday night, having bullied some of his co-workers into having a curry after the requisite gallon of lager in a Bradford pub, the boor was holding court as usual, his voice booming above the tinkle of Indian music, when he happened to rub his eye and his contact lens plopped out.

He looked for it everywhere, and harangued the others present to do likewise, but to no avail. So in an act of mock boldness, he pretended it didn't matter and continued stuffing his face regardless.

Over the ensuing months, the tight-fisted macho man – who refused to shell out on new lenses – began to get used to his one-eyed vision, even if it gave him headaches, and his workmates gradually got used to his lop-sided squint.

But one day, the bloke awoke with a searing pain in his side. Believing it was connected with the headaches, and that he was suffering from some really bad business inside, the bloke powered his XR3 straight to hospital, collapsing in the Casualty department. Appendicitis was instantly diagnosed and the bloke went under the knife.

When he regained consciousness, an out-of-focus nurse was leaning over him, holding out a small stainless steel bowl.

'Looks like you swallowed your own lens, greedy guts, and it lodged in your appendix,' she said. And she indicated the tiny optical sphere, still nestling in blood and matter on the dish.

The dopey bloke wasted no time. 'Re-sult!' he beamed, swilling it around his mouth before slipping the lens back into place before the aghast nurse could stop him.

no-*hoper*

An upper-class Cumbrian man, a manic depressive, had just been dealt another blow by Fate's fickle finger – someone had eaten the last piece of Whole Nut he'd been saving on his office desk. This was the straw that broke his psychological back. He downed a bottle of Bell's, decided he was a complete failure and better off dead, and set about ending it.

That night, he drove to a quiet spot on the coast, slung a noose over a clifftop tree branch, cocked the shotgun he'd bought earlier, and gargled down a bottle of rat poison. Then he tightened the rope around his neck and held the gun to his head, before jumping off the cliff. But as the rope took the strain, the gun was jerked away from his head, and the trigger accidentally pulled. The shot from the gun seared through the rope, leaving him to plunge into the sea below. Gulping in buckets of sea water, the would-be suicide struggled to the shore, where he violently threw up the poison.

How depressing; he was even a failure at suicide.

a close ***shave II***

Another depressive decided to take his life in the early hours of the morning in a London park. He put the gun in his mouth, pulled the trigger and shot the back of his head off. But, seemingly unaffected by the loss, he turned on his heels and walked to his nearby home. Once there he strolled into the bathroom and set about shaving as usual.

Then, and only then, did he die.

the snake ***charmer***

A friend of a friend recently returned from his honeymoon safari with his blushing bride. They'd spent two heavenly weeks under canvas in the Masai Mara getting back in touch with nature. Just themselves and the untamed beasts

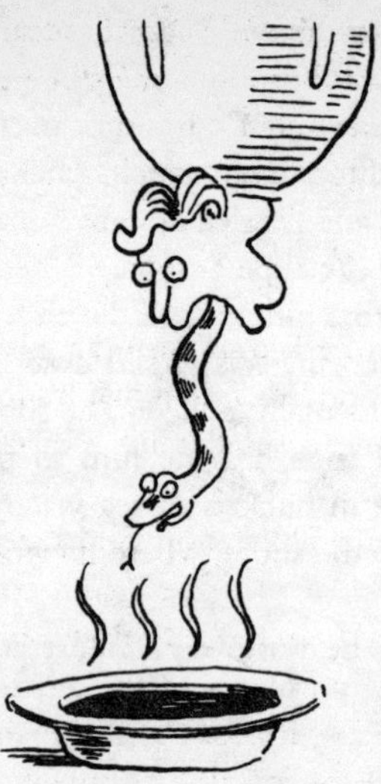

of the African plains for company – well, OK, the rest of the safari package, the drivers and the guides from the Nairobi Hilton came too. It was smashing.

After a few days back in Blighty the bloke began to feel seriously unwell. He'd lost a lot of weight – more than could be put down to normal honeymoon exertions, even though they'd not spared the horses in that department.

So he visited the doctor, who took one look at him and called an ambulance and the bloke was carted off to the hospital. When the X-rays came back the consultant, a former VSO man who was experienced in these matters, recommended a bizarre course of action.

He advised the startled patient that a snake must have crawled into his mouth when he was asleep under the stars in Africa – a common occurrence – and imparted the local wisdom on the subject. The patient, he said, must suspend himself upside down above a bowl of simmering meat broth. The reptile would soon come slithering out, unable to resist the tantalising smell.

smoking *them out*

Another chum was fresh back from an adventure holiday, rafting up the Limpopo. He found that his legs had become incredibly itchy some days after his return and consulted his local fundholder.

The medic examined him thoroughly, cupped his family jewels, asked him to turn his head and cough 'Arsenal!', then examined the patient's legs through a magnifying glass.

The poor fellow was incarcerated in the Hospital for Tropical Diseases before he could scratch, and followed the most peculiar course of medical treatment. Apparently his intumescent legs had become infested with tiny worm-like hungry parasites and there was only one known course of treatment.

Every night after dark he had to place small pieces of smokey bacon on his skin and catch the ravenous worms when they came out to feed.

> What a fanastic menagerie of imaginative parasites God endowed the world with, eh? There's the Amazon Urine Fish, for example, said to be able to detect a human trickle in the river by its warmth. The prickly beast traces the source and darts up the serpent's eye, where its spiny fins irritate to such an extent that sufferers have been known to split their difference open rather than take any more pain. Many of these creepy critters

were celebrated in the fantastic waxworks of tropical diseases in Blackpool, adults only of course, where happy holidaymakers could idle away hours giggling at grossly inflated mountains of festering flesh – or was that on the beach? We forget.

just *earsay*

An old school friend of my auntie met her in the street in Cleckheaton the other day and sadly related the tale that their old geography teacher had recently passed away.

The old chap had been a marvellous advertisement for his profession in his earlier years but apparently of late he'd become more and more dotty and had been obliged to take early retirement.

It wasn't until his sudden death and the subsequent post mortem that the reason for his deteriorating behaviour became clear. It seemed that a number of years before, on a geography field trip, an insect had drilled its way into one ear, through his brain and out through the other lughole.

The parasite had been discovered and destroyed, but no one realised it had laid its eggs in the middle of its journey. The hatched-out grubs had been eating his cerebrum ever since. By the end, sadly, he couldn't tell his ox-bow from his elbow.

thriller *from manila*

A young woman had been out in the Philippines scouting for mail-order – or is that male-order? – brides to buy. These desperate beauties were then matched back home in Grantham with rich, flabby middle-aged Englishmen that no one who wasn't completely visually impaired would touch with a barge pole of considerable dimensions.

Upon returning from her romantic mission of mercy, the matchmaker became seriously ill and was rushed into hospital, displaying a host of symptoms not even the Hospital for Tropical Diseases had witnessed before.

She was quarantined in an isolation ward but within days had died. Apparently all her blood had crystallised, like something out of *Doctor Who* or even *Oprah Winfrey.* But that's not all the top-flight medics discovered. To their horror, the new disease proved highly contagious, as everyone of them began to display the first gout-like symptoms of contamination. They were all the victims of a new and virulent plague.

Of course, it's all been hushed up.

a journey *through the interior*

A friend of an accountant we know (yes, they do have friends) took a year off and went on a trek across Africa, not on foot but by Land Rover. The route went from Cairo down through the great Rift Valley, inland, and then down south to the Cape.

There were three Land Rovers in the convoy and everyone aboard was very excited by the forthcoming adventure. After the spectacular safari animals of the Serengeti and fording river after countless river, the bloke began to feel tired and unaccountably feeble. He was still eating like a horse (in fact he was probably still eating horse, judging by the meat they'd bartered for in the last village), but felt weaker every day.

The rest of the team began to get worried, checked his temperature daily and gave him dozens of injections for every possible tropical disease, just in case. But it was to no avail and a week later he was so tired he could hardly lift a Capstan non-filter to his lips.

Lying in his tent that night and remembering Captain Oates' heroism in the face of similar travails, he staggered from his tent into the moonlit bush. The cicadas were chirruping as he fell to his knees and crawled on, deeper and deeper into the dense foliage. Eventually he could crawl no further and hauled himself up to lie back against a tree and breathe his last.

Then, as he sprawled there panting, he felt something coming forth, as a huge, sallow 28-foot-long tapeworm slithered out of his gaping mouth, and off into the jungle looking for another host.

> The best way to rid a friend – dog, child, neighbour – of a tapeworm is actually quite routine. Simply hold a piece of '*Bien fait*' cheese next to the victim's parted posterior, wait for the sinister parasite's scolex, or head, to emerge, then put your foot on in and get the host to walk away slowly, drawing out the worm's lengthy segmented body. Either that, or apply the furry part of some Velcro to the orifice – the scolex has hooks on it. Interestingly, the Japanese have the longest tapeworms. Stands to reason: they claim to have the longest intestines.

Health

* In hospitals 'bunnies' are sanitary towels and 'white mice' are tampons. Animal rights activists once misunderstood the slang and liberated twelve packs of each in a raid
* Blood is in such short supply in St Petersburg that distraught relatives have had to stop doctors secretly syphoning off the stuff from dying patients
* Capital Gold's high blood pressure football commentary has been banned from a north London hospital's cardiac ward
* In the new-style NHS, they prefer:
    - patients who can administer injections themselves
    - bystanders who know how to use drips and work dialysis machines
    - patients who bring bags of their own blood
    - wealthy people under 65
* There's a house in Liverpool entirely decorated and equipped with materials stolen from the local hospital
* President Kennedy's brain was lost in the confusion after his assassination
* People boil and explode when exposed to the vacuum of space
* Save aluminium ring-pulls – they can be exchanged for kidney dialysis machines

* Toe nails continue growing after you're dead and make unsightly holes in your best socks
* The only organ that grows continuously throughout your life is the nose (just look at your grandparents if you don't believe us)

family *fortunes*

Fateful friends and risky relatives

Uh-oh. It may be just a question of relative values sinking in the exchanges, but when you're faced with a clot in your bloodline, you just can't win. If you're looking to score maximum points of humiliation or a jackpot on the nutters' scale, call the tribe in and Bob's your uncle. 'Kin imbeciles, eh?

a real *drain*

When a man has made his mark in the world he likes to make his mark on the landscape. And the businessman who lived over the road from us was no exception. Once he'd grubbed together his pile in haberdashery, he decided to join the Surrey set, and commissioned a highly regarded builder to create his dream home, deep in the gloriously expensive countryside. The house had everything the modern family could wish for: swimming pool, barbecue patio area, sun lounge with picture windows and, best of all, a full-size snooker table and built-in bar. Magic.

The only thing that marred this modern-day Shangri-La was a large drain cover, slap bang in the middle of the driveway, right outside the front door – an inevitable legacy of the contractor's labours, and at first accepted as such.

But after a while this blot on the landscape really started to irritate the businessman and chip away at this contentment. Taking the bit between his teeth he lashed out a fortune on landscaping and transformed the carbuncle into a feature, surrounding it with a picturesque stone wall adorned with pot plants and ornamental shrubs.

Three years later the builder happened to be in the area and called in on his old client. The home owner was pleased to see the architect of his dream home, but felt the need to make a small complaint about the planning of the drainage. The perplexed builder asked to be directed to the seat of his client's discontent and was taken to the access cover outside the front door.

The builder rubbed his chin and studied the cover carefully. Then he flipped it away with his foot, exposing a virgin patch of bare earth underneath it.

Two of the worst aspects of country life, as far as urbanites are concerned, are the pitch blackness of night time and the lack of conventional toilet facilities. Happily, this next story concerns both . . .

shedding *a load*

A bloke from Bristol went to stay in the middle of the country with some old college friends who'd bought an ancient property and were 'doing it up'. Not being carrot-crunchers, the couple had rigged up some cooking facilities, but there was no electricity yet so they drove the ten miles for a take-away from the nearest curry boutique.

Swilling ale in the candlelight, the guest began to feel a pleasant state of inebriation coming on – as well as the call of nature he'd been dreading: the living room was full of masonry and dust, so God knows what the toilet would be like.

Eventually, he broached the subject, and the couple sniggered. 'It's a bit basic,' said the woman, biting her bottom lip nervously. Her partner explained the procedure. They didn't have a proper inside toilet, he explained, so he would have to find his way down the long garden to the shed, and do his business in there. 'Here,' he said, 'I should wear these if I were you.' And he handed his mate a pair of wellies, as well as some bum fodder.

Outside it was so dark you couldn't have seen one of Gyles Brandreth's sweaters if it was an inch from your face. The bloke didn't have a torch, so he had to feel his way tentatively across the boggy soil and fumble around for the outhouse. Eventually, his hands touched wood, and after a few seconds he was able to locate the door. On stepping inside, he had something of a surprise. The floor was very squelchy. 'Uh-oh,' thought the bloke, 'they haven't got round to fitting a pan yet, so they just use this as an earth toilet.' So he dropped his kecks, stooped down and relieved himself. Job done, he strode purposefully back toward the dim candlelight of the cottage.

Next morning, the bloke rose at the crack of dawn – either it was too quiet or some bird had aroused him (phwooaarr!) – and he decided he had to pay another visit to the shed.

By the cold light of day, from the outside it didn't look too bad. But inside was a real shock. Gleaming in the morning sun was an absolutely pristine avocado toilet and wash basin, all fully plumbed in, and not exactly set off by a rather nasty mess from the night before, slap bang in the middle of a new carpet.

golf *war*

A bloke at my mate's work is a keen golfer and frequently takes part in his club's charity days. He's pretty good but never wins because there's one fellow there who takes his sport very seriously and is virtually a scratch player.

On one of these competition days, the tasty golfer turned up as usual and was the first to tee off. But to the surprise of the other players, he completely fluffed his drive, fizzing it off into some bushes. Though he managed to recover on that hole, the pattern was set. When he fluffed his third tee shot in a row, hooking it out of bounds, the other competitors began to fancy their chances for real. 'He's playing like a right shanker,' muttered one.

After a dreadful nine holes out, the bloke spent a short while psyching himself up and mumbling that he couldn't possibly play as badly on the inward nine. But he was wrong. His tenth tee shot scudded along the deck, hit a bump and sailed through the air, landing just in front of a huge lake. The whole clubhouse gathered to watch what their top player would do next.

Alarmingly, the now rattled bloke completely sliced it and the ball plopped into the pond like a fishing line. A collective gasp emanated from the clubhouse as the golfer put his iron away, swung his golf bag round his head in rage and launched it into the water hazard as far as he could throw it. Then he marched, fuming, past the clubhouse, throwing his glove into a tree as he strode back towards his car.

There was a stunned silence, followed by another audible gasp as the demoralised golfer came storming past the nine-teenth again in a total strop. 'I'm having a very bad day,' he growled to the nearest contestant, and headed back at speed towards the water. Some people began to fear he might mean to do himself serious harm. After all, golf was his life.

The tension mounted as the golfer reached the lake and carried on walking until he was up to his thighs in the water. There he stopped, felt around under the surface and yanked up the water-logged golf bag he'd discarded. Then he ripped open a pocket and pulled out, to the mute amusement of all present, the dripping keys to his car.

house *of horrors*

A nice family moved into their new home, and had been saved the headache of redecorating by the previous owner. He was a dour man who'd offered the dwelling at a knock-down price because, he said, it was too big for him since his wife had left.

The only sour note was the putrid smell that seemed endemic. It was a real humdinger. After a few months, and despite the application of every type of proprietary disinfectant and bleach, as well as the dyno-rodding of the drainage system and plumbing, the stench still persisted, centred around the kitchen.

As it happened, a neighbour was standing in that very room at their cheese and wine housewarming party, held once the couple had settled in. She absentmindedly noted something odd. In her house next door there was an alcove in the wall, whereas the newcomers had a freshly wall-papered flat wall and shelving.

Without waiting for the party to clear, the host removed the shelves and broke through the plasterboard. There, in the old recess, was the reason for the festering odour: the remains of the previous owner's recently bumped-off wife.

> The classic 'hairy hand – hatchet in handbag' myth seems to haunt areas where gruesome killings have recently taken place, and the story of the young woman seduced by an enigmatic stranger who disappears and is implicated in a hideous murder becomes ubiquitous at times of headline-grabbing violent incidents. So it's only fair that the tried and tested version above reappears whenever real life conjures up a despicable man who seems to confuse homicide with DIY: notoriously, Christie of 10 Rillington Place and Dennis Nielsen, that most grotesque of Muswell Hillbillies. Nielsen features in this next anecdote.

chili *con?*

Before Dennis Nielsen was arrested for the murder and cannibalism of several young men, he was quite well-known as a union activist. A few years prior to his incarceration, his union was involved in an industrial dispute, and several of his comrades were on a long-term picket in the bitter cold of the British winter.

Morale was dropping and the food situation was grim. Then one union official popped over to give the pickets a mood-enhancing food parcel: mince, peppers and other stuff to make a delicious chili con carne. But although they had the braziers to provide heat, they lacked the necessary pots and pans for bulk cooking.

In a goodwill gesture that was to have repercussions on various stomachs after later revelations, Dennis Nielsen generously loaned them his large collection of oversized saucepans. Surprising possessions for someone who lived on his own, don't you think?

a total ***blot out***

Human balance can be affected by many things, not least drink. In fact, *mostly* drink in the largest number of cases. But everything is not what it seems with even the most innocuous of materials.

A curious rumour circulated at my girlfriend's secondary school to the effect that if you put blotting paper in the soles of your shoes it made you faint. Something to do with moisture absorption or some such. Rubbish, you might think. But nobody dared try it, even the most macho lads in the school – and they always say animals know best.

quite ***an inconvenience***

A friend of a bloke I drink with had this acquaintance from Droitwich in the deepest – or should that be dimmest? – Midlands who ran a brand new VW camper van back in the late 1970s. It was a lovely machine, all orange and white, with a sink and cooker – ideal for brewing up in those lay-bys – a bed and bunks and all the facilities except the most important, a toilet. In this bloke's case it was a particularly regrettable omission because he had the weakest bladder known to mankind – his waterworks were like a gutter system.

It was the summer holidays and the bloke was treating his family to two weeks in sunny Cornwall. Fearful of motorway snarl-ups in respect of his condition he was taking the scenic route. The bloke was enjoying quality time with his lot. They were all singing daft Brummie songs, playing spot the car transporter and listening to the Radio One Roadshow, when above all the racket he heard the call of nature. It was a call he couldn't ignore and he pulled over.

As he started hosing the hedgerow, he was horrified when a coachload of teenage schoolgirls trundled round the corner and caught him in mid-flow. There was nothing he could do but grin and bare it. The giggling multitude pressed their faces at the windows to get a good look, hooting and yelling.

A little shaken, the bloke climbed back in the cab, thinking after that embarrassment he might as well make better time and get on the motorway. An hour later though he was again busting for relief, but the next services seemed an age away. His knuckles were white as he held on for dear life. At last he spotted the slip road to a pub restaurant and he swerved into the car park.

Leaping from the camper, he hobbled across the gravel in agony, dived into the bar and sprinted towards the gents sign on the door opposite. He was so desperate that he unzipped his fly as he ran and readied himself for action. Crashing through the door with everything in hand, he was horrified to find himself in the restaurant, face-to-face with the coachload of screaming girls who'd seen all too much of him earlier on.

Sadly, on his way out he was grabbed by the fuzz –

police, that is – hauled off to the slammer and charged on two counts of indecent exposure.

seam *rolled*

The wear and tear on a modern driveway can leave the entrance to many a modern home shoddy and riddled with potholes. Thank heavens then for charitable gangs of roadlayers who often seem to find that they have over-ordered just enough materials to resurface the odd private drive for a small consideration in cash.

So it was with a woman up the road from a friend in Derbyshire, who was impressed by an enthusiastic Irishman in a new BMW. He ran through his patter: 'Tarmac left over from nearby road job [blah blah blah]', and agreed a very reasonable price to lay the woman's approach.

The gang duly turned up the next day bang on the nail and set to work with great gusto and a shovel. The woman was so pleased with her negotiation skills that she left them to it and went off to reward her good sense by spending the money she'd saved on a little something for herself.

She arrived back just after teatime, loaded down with shopping bags, as the road gang were applying the top dust coating. The gaffer explained that the dust layer was needed to help the tarmac bond together and she should leave it undisturbed for a few days or she'd have people walking tar all over her best living room carpet. She knew only too well from bitter experience that tar and a deep shag didn't mix, so she heeded the advice and left the driveway to cure properly. The woman was so chuffed with the shiny black driveway that she handed over the readies with a flourish and chucked in a bit extra for a drink for the lads. They departed all smiles.

A week or so later the woman took out her yard brush and set about shifting the top dust coat. To her horror, she found that she'd been ripped off something awful. For instead of a brand spanking new tarmac driveway, she had two inches of nutty slack coal steamrollered atop her old drive.

a strange *turnout*

Some newly-wed friends of our kid hocked themselves up to the eyeballs to buy a recently built detached house on an exclusive executive homes development in rustic Stoke. The area was fully landscaped, offering a tantalising choice of three and four bedroom thatched neo-Georgian properties with all mod cons.

But after only a few months of wedded bliss something started getting right up their nose – a peculiar smell that seemed to penetrate every room of the house.

A call alerted the builders and they came scurrying round to investigate the hum. They checked interior plumbing: all tickerty-boo; then the drains: clean as a whistle. Nothing amiss.

Then finally, in desperation, they removed a couple of bricks to check the air flow. At last they'd got to the bottom of the problem. Almost literally. The cavity wall was caked solid with waste materials diverted on their way to the sewage farm.

going, going, *totally gone . . .*

Most airports have auctions every now and then to get rid of items from the unclaimed baggage department which are occupying valuable space. One bloke I know always goes down there and bids for the wallets.

He reckons he's going to get lucky and find one the Aga Khan's lost or something. But strangely people seem invariably to lose their wallets when they are empty, because there's never a sign of any cash when my mate gets hold of them.

Another regular down at these scavenging sessions, er, auctions, a young housewife, spotted a bargain she couldn't overlook and snapped up half a dozen packets of a popular proprietary washing powder.

Pleased with her haul at first, she soon complained to the manufacturers when her washing not only failed the window tests, but – contrary to the folklore of TV advertising – she would have happily swapped two packets of her new powder for one of her old brand that Danny Baker had nicked off her.

It was rubbish. It didn't shift stains in the slightest and the residue of deep-down, ground-in-dirt meant her whites weren't bright whites anymore.

The puzzled company sent a sample away for analysis and discovered the reason for her wash-day blues. The woman had purchased six 30-kg boxes of pure heroin, and at a very good price too.

how *ferry sad*

There are many small ferries around the country that are a lifeline to the small local communities they serve. A pen-pusher who went on the same assertiveness training course as a defrocked priest from the Trossachs was a regular commuter on the Plymouth to Torpoint ferry. This small vessel plies its trade between the humming metropolis and the dormitory towns that feed this seafaring municipality, bringing comfort and culture to these far-flung outposts of civilisation (what – in Devon?)

The officer worker in question was climbing slowly up the career ladder and after years of brown-nosing and arse-shining had just been promoted to deputy chief assistant filing clerk in charge of paper clips, albeit while someone was away on maternity leave. He'd celebrated this surge in his life plan by purchasing a new pair of luminous bicycle-clips and proudly sported them that evening on his ride home.

The ferry was his link with his country roots and, mindful of his mother having his tea on the table regular as clockwork, the chap set off from his office dead on the stroke of five, in plenty of time to reach the dockside and catch the ferry. But then the fickle finger of Fate picked him out for a seeing to and his front tyre blew out before he'd got halfway. Pulling out the offending rusty nail with his teeth, the petty bureaucrat snapped open his puncture repair kit and went for the yellow chalk, then abraded the surface, splurged rubber solution and applied the patch in a time Nigel Mansell's pit crew would have been proud to achieve.

Vaulting back on his bicycle, he knew he'd be late so he peddled for all he was worth to make the jetty in time.

Cresting the hill above the dockside and observing the ferry leaving port, his skinny legs disappeared in a flurry of pinstripe as he streaked down the hill and thundered along the pier, building up to a crescendo of speed. The hurtling cyclist sprang from the dockside in a devil-may-care attempt to mimic one of Evel Knievel's death-defying leaps.

But in a cruel twist of fate the bloke had misjudged his lateness as well as the distance. The ferry was in fact coming in to dock, and he crashed into the water just ahead of its bow which unyieldingly mangled his frame against the quayside.

the legal *eagle*

Some time in the 1950s a five-year-old girl was staying with her grandmother on the rural baronial estate of an old lord, a bigwig in the legal profession. Not quite as barking as a judge, but definitely two briefs short of a portfolio.

One day, his antique lordship paid the lowly subjects a social visit (making sure they weren't burning his wood on their fire, or enjoying the eggs from his chickens, that sort of thing). His ruddy face bursting with supercilious good humour, the ancient blue-blood spotted the young girl and – as they do – immediately tried to get her on his knee.

'Well, well, my young lady,' he tweeded, slavering, 'how are you enjoying my hospitality?' The little girl said nothing. The older woman, not wanting any trouble, nudged her granddaughter to respond. But the florid old fogy was unperturbed.

'What's the matter, young missie?' he cooed. 'Never seen a JP before?'

'No,' retorted the screw-faced scamp, 'But Oi seen a sparrow poo!'

on the *skids*

A friend of our dentist – he's something big in the City; a skyscraper? – did very well during the economic miracle of the 1980s until the over-inflated bubble burst along with his prospects. While the money was rolling in, this prat of blue-blooded stock and his gilt-edged wife had sent their youngest son to one of England's swankiest public schools to give him the benefit of a privileged egocentric education.

But the river of cash had dried to a trickle and they were forced to trade down from their country mansion with servants to a recently repossessed semi. As part of the rescheduling of their massive debt, they also had to send their spoilt brat to the local county primary.

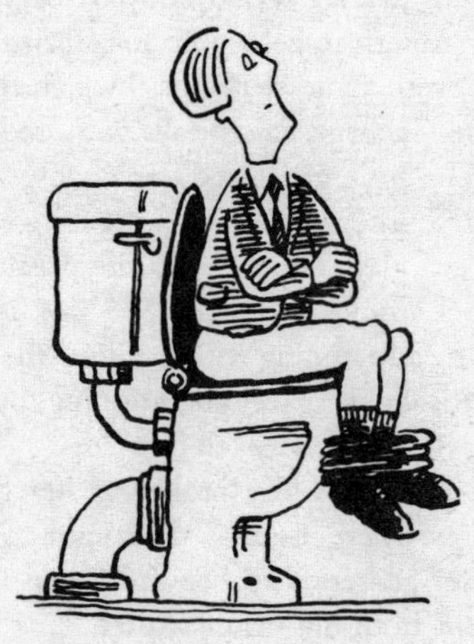

The downgraded little Lord Snooty had considerable difficulty fitting in with his reduced circumstances and on his very first day got into hot water. He'd politely raised his hand to ask if he could visit the toilet but disappeared for an inordinate length of time. After twenty minutes, the indignant teacher set out to discover the new boy's whereabouts.

The fledgling toff was sitting on the lavatory with the door open wide and regarded the prof haughtily, as if there was a bad smell under his nose. The teacher was furious. 'What the hell do you think you're doing, lad?' he stormed.

'Sorry, master,' crooned the boy ingratiatingly. 'I know I've been some time, but I'm still awaiting the arrival of the person who wipes the bottoms round here.'

dead *cert*

Another young friend was overjoyed to receive one of those spooky American baby dolls for Christmas. The life-like replica even came with its own birth certificate, much like the Cabbage Patch dolls you used to get a few years back. The little girl loved her cuddly baby doll and the two became inseparable.

The little girl played house with the plastic baby substitute, pushing it around in a pram. She gave it tea and even did the washing and ironing with the doll. She made believe with this politically incorrect conditioning toy until the sad worn-out plaything literally fell to pieces.

The poor angel was heartbroken at her favourite toy's demise. But nowhere near as distraught as the day she opened a letter addressed to her and found inside a death certificate, sent from the manufacturer.

the high *jump*

A fellow from Dagenham was cajoled, against his better judgement, into going bungee jumping with colleagues from work. They were all there, including one notoriously macho show-off scaffolder, built like a brick sh . . . out-house and a real action man. No challenge was too much for him: windsurfing, free-fall parachuting, mountain surfing – he'd even done the Cresta Run on a hot water bottle.

The bungee ropes were suspended from an immense crane towering over the local docks. A lift took them up the tower to the gantry and, as luck would have it, the nervous rookie got paired off with Mr Macho and his bragging motormouth. His ludicrous banter about how he'd seen it all before irked the instructor and his apprehensive workmate alike.

At the top the gloater skipped out on to the crane arm, smirking and leering at his mates below. Then the instructor shouted 'Go!' and the loudmouth leapt forward. But the instructor made as if to grab him back, yelling, 'Not you – I haven't tied you on properly yet!' Of course this wasn't true; just the callous instructor's bowel-loosening joke to bring the braggart back down to earth.

a queer *reason*

An Antipodean chum works in the visa department of the Australian Embassy and was surprised when an old cockney character, at least 80 years young, tottered into the office asking for the necessary paperwork to emigrate.

The desk clerk gently proffered the observation that the

chap was way over the normal age limit and asked him why he was so keen to start a new life down under.

'Is it to be with your family?' he enquired.

'No,' replied the old cove. 'They all live in Essex.'

'Health reasons then?'

'Nope. Fit as a fiddle that's never been played.'

'Then perhaps you could tell me why you're so keen to leave the country,' retorted the paper shuffler.

'Well, it's them new homosexuality laws,' the old codger grumbled. 'It used to be illegal under 21, then they legalised it for 18-year-olds – I want to get out before they make it compulsory.'

The facts of life

- Rather than use the inadequate toilet facilities, football supporters standing on terraces generally rolled up their match programmes and directed their urine into the pocket of the person in front
- An accounts department once explained to a creditor, 'Sorry your cheque isn't included with this letter, but unfortunately I have already sealed the envelope. Yours etc . . .'
- After a sharp blow to the head, chances are you'll come to speaking a strange foreign language absolutely fluently
- Soldiers break their marching step when crossing bridges because a British army platoon once destroyed one with its vibrations
- Everyone's seen an irritating macho man run down the beach, dive in and surface minus trunks
- Anglers often land a 14lb pike, and discover a 1lb trout in its mouth attached to their hook
- A top fashion designer once produced a top-of-the-range swimsuit that went transparent when wet because he didn't believe his creations should be treated as functional
- Every cellar in Bristol was once prison to an African slave

* Undertakers' tricks of the trade:
  - remove the deceased's brain and pack the head with newspaper so the eyes stay in place
  - if the cadaver's too big for the coffin, break the ankles and bend the feet sideways – no one will ever know
* You can see stars in broad daylight when you stand at the bottom of a deep well
* The Procter & Gamble man in the moon logo is a secret satanic sign (of course it's not!)
* The British Post Office can deliver anything, no matter how stupid the sender has been – one package addressed to 'Arij Aba' eventually found its way to the rightful recipient: someone in Harwich Harbour
* Lighting a match in a room quickly clears up even the most noxious fart
* Committing suicide always earns an 'A' in exams
* During the Gulf War, Iraq's siren of propaganda, Baghdad Betty, broadcast to allied forces that a famous TV star was sleeping with their wives and girlfriends back home. Unfortunately she picked Bart Simpson

food *and drink*

Indigestible anecdotes

Those of a cultured palate may find an unhealthy diet of excessive consumption hard to stomach. But check out this menu of *à la carte* codswallop, where the over-indulgent always get their just desserts. Swill it round your mouth and sample the Goolden delights of, oh, chicken cyst, human knuckle . . . ooh and there's some Chinaman's head, I'm sure . . .

the *prime cut*

A friend of a friend, a West Country campsite owner-cum-gentleman farmer, was wending his way down the narrow country lanes one dark and stormy night towards his little patch of olde England ('Caravans welcome. No bikers. No travellers.')

Normally, he strictly obeyed the unwritten rules of rural motoring, i.e. hurtled down the snaking road at breakneck speed taking the corners on the wrong side of the road and blasting his horn at any stray animals that got in the way. But this particular night there was a large white refrigerated lorry clogging up the road – a red rag to a bull. The truck was rattling along at a hell of a lick, but the impatient bloke driving along behind it was fuming and weaving around looking for a passing place. Just then the lorry clattered over a pot-hole. The back door flew open and a solid muslin sack bounced out on to the road. The bloke slammed on the anchors, skidded to a halt and snatched up the cold package; it was too good an opportunity to miss. Through the drizzly headlights he saw the chunky bag was marked 'Lamb' and happily tossed it in the car, drooling all the way home at the bonus of a roast for supper.

He handed his surprised wife the package on his way through to the telly but was alarmed by a scream and loud thud as the poor woman collapsed.

It was soon clear why. In the cold light of the kitchen, the bloke realised that the sack was actually marked 'Limb' – it apparently contained an amputated leg originally *en route* from hospital to incinerator.

bottoms *up*

A Surreyman from Yorkshire lived in New Zealand back in the 1970s and gained some fascinating insights into the interdependency of the indigenous Maoris and more recent arrivals.

One wily old native New Zealander who lived on the outskirts of Nelson had a large family to feed and very little to do it with, so he had to rely on his wits. Luckily there was enough in that department to sustain an army.

The picturesque centrepiece of the municipality of Nelson is a large ornamental pond which is home to a wide and colourful variety of wildfowl. As students of economics will know, what we have here is an obvious case of supply and demand. Sadly, as in many commercial situations, there were problems, i.e. how to supply the ducks to his demanding family without attracting the attention of the authorities and leading them to interfere in the free function of his moral obligations. Luckily these problems were overcome with impressive enterprise.

Apparently the breadwinner had some metal rat traps welded up to his own specifications which he would load with cheese. These he would place in the shallows of the pond late at night. Then he'd return at first light before the pond authorities or general public could poke their noses in and harvest the ducks, bobbing with their bottoms up.

In this manner he could feed his entire family at surprisingly little cost to himself.

overloaded, ***over here***

Three Kentish sauce merchants drove over to France in a big old Volvo estate to stock up on liquid refreshment.

The jalopy handled the journey to one of the Cinque Ports and across the pond with some ease. Only the ridiculous quantity of alcoholic beverages crammed into it on the way back from the Gallic hypermarket presented a challenge it seemed unlikely to survive. However, a few heart-stopping phuts and nasty clunks apart, it ran pretty well.

Confidently, then, the lads chucked down as much as they could on the ferry crossing and piled into the old wagon when it was time to disembark. Revving up, the motor still sounded fine and they drove out on to British soil again.

But for some reason things seemed a lot worse than before – perhaps it was the sea crossing. After a few miles they lost the exhaust on a sleeping policeman (served him right).

A few hundred yards further and there was a wholesale collapse of the suspension. The passengers were at first mystified – the old crate had been giving such a good account of itself. But when they began to remove some of the booze, they soon discovered what had broken the car's back: two big Eastern Europeans had stowed away in the boot.

> The cross-channel-ferry trafficking of cheap plonk and slop since the virtual ending of Customs restrictions under the Single Market has already spawned its own mythology. There are some who hold forth about the number of chancers with 'specialist car axle repair centres' springing up near to where the weighed-down cars and vans come creaking off the boats. Add to that list the existing plethora of apocryphal stories concerning the Channel Tunnel, as featured in *Return of Urban Myths*. For instance, the Chunnel management claim there's no chance whatsoever of a leak in the roof of the tunnel, but nevertheless demanded that all suppliers waterproof their equipment. Also there will apparently be special observation cars where lucky Club Class passengers will be able to see the flourishing marine life of the English Channel through special windows in the tunnel walls. From the Queen's opening on, you'll have to endure a right royal selection of trans-*Manche* twaddle to take us cringing into the twenty-first century.

a little *whine?*

The scheming manager of a pretentious bistro in Dover was one of the first to exploit the possibilities of buying his plonk from France where excise is lower than here. He knackered his old jalopy by making fifteen trips to the land of garlic and striped shirts in the first six months, and he had a close shave when the French Customs officers had a birthday party in his eaterie. It's illegal to sell wine bought from abroad without paying a slice to the Treasury, and it was only their inability to *parler français* that prevented the duty men from discovering what was – quite literally – under their noses.

Tight as he was, the bistro boss learned his lesson and decided to return to his local sources for vino in future. Until, that is, some chancer who supplied his mood-sculpting easy listening tapes happened to mention the possibility of getting hold of several casks of red wine. Most importantly, it was dirt cheap.

Under cover of darkness a few days later, like latter-day smugglers the two conspirators were emptying a combi van of its barrels of grape-derived fluid. Clandestine activities completed, money was exchanged for goods.

The next day, the revenue men were back in. With some confidence, nay a knowing smirk, the manager recommended the house red to complement their soup-in-a-basket main meals. They concurred and a carafe, decanted from one of the barrels, was brought through for tasting. A glass was poured and an officer took a big slurp. Instantly, he retched and spat out the whole lot, spluttering and spitting. The manager looked on in horror – he hadn't had time to taste it himself. Then the duty man recovered and screamed at the top of his voice, 'Are you trying to poison me? That stuff's saltier than a trawlerman's trollop!'

It seems the knocked-off vino collapso had been half-inched from a frozen food factory, where red cooking wine is routinely salted before becoming part of the nutritious *coq au vin*.

slap *happy*

A retired seafarer, who was known to an habitual ale-swilling acquaintance, always frequented the same pub in Cleethorpes and regularly met up with a motley crew of his old shipmates to swap tales, drink to excess and generally have a good crack.

The poor seaman had been deaf in one ear for as long as he could remember and always took up the end pew to get his good ear in pole position so his cronies couldn't make any jokes at his expense. One evening one of the crusty old salts was spinning a rip-roaring yarn punctuated with saucy hilarity, causing the deaf codger to guffaw just as he was taking a sup from his mild.

The belly laugh became a violent coughing fit. Luckily, one sharp-thinking ancient mariner sprang up and gave him a stout wallop on the back. Something torpedoed out of the old seadog's bad ear and on to the table: it was a corporation bus ticket, issued in 1940. And to the salt's glee, its removal restored his quota of good ears to the usual complement.

The old bloke was apparently so overjoyed at the restoration of his faculties that he splashed out on a round for everyone in the alehouse – all three of them.

Some stories just push credibility a little too far. I mean, really, a Yorkshireman buying a round? Here's another version of the 'unusual things jammed in orifices' strand, though by no means as painful or as embarrassing as some we could mention (and probably will). Similar in form to the old lady and aurally-lodged tooth in *The Return of Urban Myths* but with a nice nautical flavour and a large pinch of salt.

a stiff *drink*

It's well known that medical students are a bunch of pranksters. Our local GP – sorry, fundholder – went to college with a clutch of aspiring Kildares that were always up to high jinks. Deeply committed though they were to their studies and desperate to dedicate their young lives selflessly to helping others, they did like a drink. Well, they were doctors, weren't they? And they liked nothing more than winding up the crusty old landlord of their local hostelry, who only put up with them out of respect to their noble calling and the extraordinarily long hours junior doctors have to put in – some of them were in his boozer from 11 until 11.

One night the irrepressible japesters borrowed a recently dressed corpse from anatomy class. They dressed it up as your standard medic – an old school tie, tweeds and varsity scarf – then took it for a night on the town.

Dragging the stiff round various bars, they passed it off remarkably convincingly as a paralytic medic they were shouldering around. Eventually they rolled into the local, bundled into a corner and rapidly filled the table with empty glasses.

Come chucking-out time they were pratically comatose themselves and absent-mindedly left the pub body-less.

Minutes later the grumpy landlord got fed up with the verbal approach to bar emptying and angrily shook the unresponsive customer. To his horror the pallid corpse keeled forward, scattering pint pots from the table. The horrified publican gasped for air, clutched his chest and dropped down dead from a heart attack.

Sadly, there were no doctors around to revive him.

high *tea*

My mate's mother from Yorkshire had a friend who was busy serving dinner to one of her corporate high-flier husband's important potential clients. The deal under discussion was not only a big one, but crucial to her hubby's company's survival in these straightened times and the meal, though pleasant, had been a little strained.

Then it emerged in conversation that it was the client's wife's birthday, and a stroke of inspiration came to the hostess. She knew that her son, a dab hand in the kitchen, had baked a lovely-looking cake earlier that day and it was still in the fridge.

So, dousing the cake with icing sugar and dusting off a candle, she made a grand entrance and carved each of the delighted guests a huge slice of the distinctively flavoured treat.

From that point on it was a cruise all the way. The conversation flowed like a babbling brook and the foursome got on like a house on fire, chattering away until the early hours when they all began yawning.

The deal was sealed and the evening was declared such a hit that the new-found friends gleefully arranged to go out on the town the same time next week. Tired and happy, the hosts waved goodbye and toddled off to bed.

Over breakfast the next morning the mother explained to her son that she'd appropriated his cake in an emergency but she would happily buy him another to make amends. Imagine her surprise when the shiftless lad demanded £17 – in lieu of the potent hashish cake they'd scoffed the night before.

> It's not known whether the family had a budgie or canary (not so fashionable these days), but if they had, the reefer-toking son would have had a ready source to provide full harvests of cannabis. Hemp (or marijuana) seed, used in standard bird feed, has to be sterilised before packing – it's the law of the land – but the process of working its way through a caged bird's digestive system is said to reverse the seed's infertility. Hence the phrase, 'This is good shit, maan.'

labelling under ***a misapprehension***

When out shopping, most people who come to this country without a grasp of the native tongue rely, reasonably enough, on the labels of canned food to accurately illustrate their contents. Recent migrants hailing from the Far East often buy clearly labelled tinned cat or dog at the supermarket but are mystified why they are unable to get hold of the fresh variety at the local butcher.

> The next tale also features unfounded prejudice and fear of the unknown, i.e. foreign muck, as our less cosmopolitan countrymen would style anything beyond the realms of meat and two veg. There are long and contradictory traditions here: first that the best places to eat foreign food are where the people of that nationality choose to eat it (although this is countered by the fact that they have 'more robust stomachs' or more grit in their intestines); and second that every town has a Chinese/Indian/Malaysian/Thai restaurant that has been done for having cats/Alsatians/rats in their cold store. The next targets will be those Japanese sushi bars. No doubt there'll be rumours that they serve up all the stuff raw!

the fist *anniversary*

A trawlerman's wife, who works out at the same aerobics class as a friend of our Beryl, was being taken out to celebrate her first wedding anniversary by her windswept husband. She was dressed up to the tens (that smart!) and he tugged on his best Arran jumper for an evening drenched in romance at the local Chinese.

For a change they didn't order a set meal for two but, carried away by the occasion, plunged headlong into the *à la carte* selections. Lambrusco chilling on ice, they tucked into the first course, a selection of sweet and sour – much like their topsy-turvy marriage, really.

Suddenly the woman began to choke and coughed up a small, half-chewed bone into her napkin. Then she blew her nose as a diversionary device and popped the napkin into her pocket without another thought.

The rest of the meal was marvellous, rounded off by her favourite treat, a mountain of banana fritters smothered in syrup. The bill wasn't too steep either and as they meandered back arm-in-arm, hubby suggested a night cap at the local.

Snuggled up in the corner, the bloke tucked into his lager top and his happy spouse sipped her Bailey's. They'd happened to find a table next to a bunch of old doctors from the locality celebrating a win on the horses.

Suddenly the woman felt a sneeze coming on and whipped out her napkin. The bone from the meal tumbled out and rolled across the table, coming to rest against one of the old medics' leather elbow patches.

The assembled doctors went very quiet and one of them picked up the bone and examined it closely. He spoke very slowly.

'What a peculiar thing to carry around. Where did you get this?' he asked gravely.

The woman explained.

'Oh dear,' continued the venerable quack. 'Unless I'm very much mistaken, I think you'll find that it's a metacarpal – a human knuckle to you, madam!'

> Of course, cockneys who step out of line have been eating knuckle sandwiches for years. Take Courage before you read this next tale of ill-advised deceit . . .

a bitter *top*

Twenty years ago a friend's stepdad habitually visited a pub, where the landlord was known far and wide for his parsimonious nature. It was the kind of place where you never accepted a pint pulled in the other bar for fear of being served a hybrid half-litre of mixed slops with a 'top' made up of corporation pop – tap water.

The beer was not only watered but the crisps were almost lapping their sell-by dates – as chewy as a marathon runner's feet. Hygienically the pub made Dirty Dick's look like an operating theatre. But the mild was a penny cheaper than elsewhere and the convention of licensing hours was conscientiously ignored.

In an effort to increase his profit margin further, the

skinflint publican decided to recycle the beer slops in the drip trays under the beer taps by pouring them back in the barrels. He wanted his staff to pour all the spilt lager in one bucket and bitter in another, 'so the brewery could see just how much was being wasted'.

Down in the cellar that night the penny-pincher encountered a problem. He couldn't figure out the pressurised system on a new keg and was about to resort to the 'Bristol screwdriver' method – whacking it with a hammer – when his spanner slipped. In an instant, the tap shot out of the barrel with such force that it took his head clean off his shoulders, giving the poor bloke his last orders.

Consumption

* There's a restaurant in Japan where, provided you pay the price, you can smash up all the crockery
* There's an eccentric pub in Hertfordshire that selects its own weird opening hours, and charges anything from a halfpenny 'in the old money' to £50 for two pints
* There are liqueur-style chocolates on sale in Amsterdam that have human blood in the liquid centre
* Other fondant selections on sale around the world include chocolates from Egypt with beetles inside and a French alternative, small dried frogs (of course)
* When Newcastle's Peter Beardsley was first called up for England, he nipped to a nearby Rowntree's factory and bought a tray of ha'penny chocolate misshapes to take down with him as a treat. 'Ee, the lads'll love these,' he said, inaccurately
* If you leave a tooth in a cup of fizzy cola overnight, it completely dissolves. As does a penny piece left in tomato sauce for long enough
* If you don't have one of the colours in your Smarties packet, write off and complain – they'll send you a load in the post
* Beware the chicken burger – that luxury 'mayonnaise' may turn out to be a cyst on the fowl

that's *showbiz*

Fame and misfortune

Stars in your eyes and Uranus in full view: you can't fail to see the ugly side of the beautiful people. This glittering procession of the great and the good shows a right royal variety of performances, from top billing balderdash to acts with no visible means of support. It's not all glamour . . .

ou *idiot*

The Open University is a fine institution that has provided hope and opportunity for a wide range of intelligent people who wouldn't normally have been granted access to the traditional university system.

Working from the comfort of home, OU students often have jobs, homes and families to take care of as well as getting up at the crack of dawn and working late into the night to complete assignments. It's not all mumbling, bearded 1970s rejects in crimplene suits warbling on about quantum physics before *The Big Breakfast*.

But many who cruised through college freebasing drugs on Daddy's silver spoon and dashing off the occasional essay still look down their noses at red brick universities – and even further down at the Open University graduates.

Apparently, when the late, demented Sir Keith Joseph was Minister for (destruction of) Education and Science he decided to visit the Open University to see what made it tick. He and his entourage cruised into Milton Keynes in their Daimlers and were met by the Vice Chancellor, accountants, administrators – in fact all the people who matter, even the senior academics. Sir Keith was wheeled around the university buildings, nodding studiously all the while. Stopping only for lunch before heading back to Westminster, Sir Keith was wined and dined and toasted (if only) by the assembled eminent profs, fearful of their futures.

Replete, Sir Keith was escorted back to his waiting limo but, just as he got to the open door, he turned on his hosts.

'Haven't you forgotten something?' he rebuked them.

The befuddled academics cast around. 'Er, well not that we can think of,' they replied in confusion. (A language Joseph spoke fluently.)

'Really,' admonished an irate Sir Keith. 'You haven't shown me the halls of residence yet!'

disney *cover-up*

The onset of the video age in the 1970s and 1980s ushered in the updating of the Walt Disney Corporation's naive marketing style into a cynically smart operation. One of the new policies was the selective release of beloved classics for public purchase. Clearly the classic fairy-tale animation *Snow White* had to be lined up for release, and so the technical department were asked to prepare it for video consumption.

Late one night one of the more inquisitive engineers viewed it all the way through and sensed there was something not quite right about it. Luckily, after a few hours' painstaking examination, he located the source of the problem: a number of single frames revealed Snow White in all her naked nubile glory.

At the time of the making of the film, a few subliminal tasteful glimpses were obviously seen as a way to appeal to horny fathers in the cinema audience, but in the age of the VHS freeze-frame, such scenes clearly wouldn't win over America's moral majority.

Needless to say – and to prevent you having to check for yourselves – the offending peep show element has now been removed.

> Subliminal cuts have a long and controversial history in the cinema. In the movie *Bedtime for Bonzo*, for example, scenes involving (alleged) FBI informer and future president Ronald

Reagan were intercut with quick flashes of a chimpanzee to subconsciously improve Raygun's intellectual profile. As to that *Snow White* story, the same spurious idea has been associated with *Who Framed Roger Rabbit* – which supposedly has nude flicks of Jessica Rabbit. Poor old Disney is the butt of so many myths, notably the virulent one about child-slavery kidnapping which we recorded in *The Return of Urban Myths*. The latest dollop of Disney fantasia suggests that the cover of *The Little Mermaid* features an accurate drawing of a huge male appendage. We've stood in Woolworth's for an hour researching this matter, but all we got were crabs on the rocks.

blarney *baloney*

Apparently when James Galway was at the peak of his popularity in the 1970s, taking the world by storm with his charismatic, fruity flutery, he bought himself a gleaming black German sports car that soon became the apple of his eye. Next on the list, as the money came rolling in, was a flash new mansion in a salubrious part of rural Ireland. Old swivel-eyes loved Ireland and its wonderful people.

Soon after the move, he was approached by a couple of odd-jobbing cowboys. You could hear their spurs chink as they walked up the front path in their cheap, too-small overalls. 'Mr Galway,' one of them said, 'we're down on our luck and are in need of gainful employment – any chance of a crack here?'

Galway was moved by the appeal from his fellow

countrymen and stroked his beard while he pondered on what they could do.

'How much would you charge to paint my porch glossy pink?'

'Fifty pound.'

'Done,' said Galway, nipping in to hand them the money and the paint. Then he picked up his jacket and went for a stroll and a whistle in the countryside.

An hour later he was sauntering back. As he approached his house, though, he had the shock of his life. For there, glinting in the driveway, hand-painted from bumper to bumper in sickly pink, was his new Porsche.

recipe ***for disaster***

Some time in the 1970s, renowned TV cook Fannie Cradock and her monocle-clad, beleaguered spouse, Johnnie, were doing their usual routine on the box, showing how to make cakes with a delicious crumbly quality.

Fannie, as was her wont, came up with a few smart tips

in the cake stakes, and when the 'one that was made earlier' emerged, it was a fantastic, mouthwatering example of the culinary art. Johnnie, who had had little to say up to this point, looked on admiringly and then confidently declared, 'Follow that recipe and all your cakes will look like Fannie's'.

> There are plenty of tales about shy, retiring Bob Monkhouse, and he's been around long enough to recognise a good anecdote when he sees one. One actual incident said a lot about the great unwashed's listening habits. A man from Dudley was asked to name a composer beginning with 'V'. Without hesitation he answered confidently, 'Violinski'.

family ***misfortune***

Bob Monkhouse was apparently hosting *Family Fortunes* during rehearsals and one set of relatives taking part faced an insurmountable problem – a grandmother with all the intelligence of a snail with a lobotomy.

The aim of the game was to pick an answer that a random cross-section of the public would agree with. It didn't look hopeful: several easy questions drew blanks from the antique answerer (e.g. Bob: 'Name something pink': Gran: 'My cardigan').

But what topped the lot was the response to the challenge to 'Name something deserted in winter'. The clueless dame thought for a second, then shouted, 'My sister!'

Monkhouse was apparently taken aback and tried gently

to convince her that she might wish to revise her response, maybe in favour of Goodison Park, or a cricket ground.

The woman remained adamant, though. 'Nope, my sister. That swine of a husband left her and took everything with him!'

belly *full*

A glam pop singer in the 1980s was always having spurious allusions drawn about his sexuality. This was partly because so many girlfriends found his androgynous looks enticing, but also because he dressed one shade more reserved than Danny La Rue.

One night, it's said, he was due to perform live on stage at a gala of top popsters. His third single had just entered the charts, and the crowd were chanting his name in anticipation. But delay followed delay.

At one stage the master of ceremonies approached the microphone to announce that the star would be out soon: 'He's got his hands full at the moment dealing with some fans back in the dressing room, as you can imagine.'

Then the lights dimmed, and the effeminate pop star emerged into a fog of dry ice and flashing lights. The opening bars to his latest hit song resounded around the arena. But as the new romantic singer began his sexual gyrations, he suddenly stiffened and collapsed.

Curtains were drawn and paramedics rushed on, quickly hustling the hot property off to the nearest Casualty department, where doctors diagnosed a severe groin pain.

Swiftly, arrangements were made for his stomach to be pumped and the extracts were analysed thoroughly. The examining consultant – who considered himself a broad-minded fellow – was shocked but impressed by what he found: the singer's stomach was filled with a pint and a half of sperm.

a singer's *lot*

A friend had landed his first big role as an opera singer, even if it was in a Gilbert and Sullivan show. It had been a struggle for him to find anything prestigious before because his memory was so bad. I'll tell you another thing: he had a terrible memory.

But in this case his voice was sufficiently good – a lovely rounded bass – to warrant the producer giving him a chance to prove he could cope. The role was that of the famous Tax Collector and, as a concession, the stage director allowed the singer to have a crib sheet positioned in the pit to remind him of his words.

On the opening night, the bass crooner paid more than the standard number of visits to the toilet facilities, but his voice was in good shape. On cue, he strolled confidently onstage and positioned himself in front of his idiot board. The band struck up his theme, and a deep, rich timbre filled the theatre.

Sadly, hazards lie in wait for the unwary. The words of the song go, 'My stately pen is never lax/When I'm assessing income tax'. Unfortunately, the mischievous scamp who'd felt-tipped the words on to the card had neglected to leave a space between 'pen' and 'is', and the nervous artiste simply sang what he read, bringing a right royal flush to his cheeks – and a raising a few eyebrows among the genteel ladies in the boxes.

Entertainment

- ✱ When shown in Japan *Monty Python's Flying Circus* was translated as 'Gay Boy's Dragon Show'
- ✱ In London there's a bar themed around Rolf Harris and festooned with memorabilia of the great Aussie entertainer. One night he turned up, and all present greeted him with chants of 'Rolf! Rolf!'
- ✱ Soul singer Otis Redding was so stoned on coke he insisted on flying the plane that crashed and killed him
- ✱ Tattoo transfers of Mickey Mouse, dosed up with LSD and Ecstasy, have been sold outside infant schools to get the kids hooked
- ✱ Disney myths:
  - ■ Female employees aren't allowed to wear trousers or crop their hair
  - ■ Male employees aren't permitted to grow beards
  - ■ If you say 'Humpy pumpy' to Snow White at any of the Disney parks, she'll blow your nose
  - ■ Every Disney park has a network of huge subterranean labyrinths – Princess Di knows them intimately
  - ■ There's a covert hard-drinking society called 'Club 33' based in New Orleans Square, Disneyland. Make the secret sign, get a drink

- ■ Disabled visitors with one wheelchair attendant always go to the front of the queue for rides

- ✻ The movie *Three Men and A Baby* has a scene with a real ghost in it
- ✻ The lead singer of a world-famous pop group forced his publishing company to sign a huge deal with a new band – their manager was caught running drugs through Customs for the high-profile vocalist and took the rap to maintain the star's anti-drugs image

for *adults only*

XXXXXX-rated crudités

A little carnal knowledge is a dangerous thing. And so is love, according to this *menage à* try-anything-once from our world-renowned Institute of Scatology: this alternative lovers' guide poses more sexual dilemmas than Rod Hull and Emu. The flesh may be weak, but the punters are gagging for it.

on *the pull*

A mobile phone salesman who convinced a foolhardy workmate to sign on the dotted line was a bit of a wow with the ladies, or so he claimed.

One night a few months back he'd inveigled himself into an upmarket drinks party and was cruising the room with his eyes peeled for talent.

Then it happened: instant animal attraction. She caught his gaze and then held it hard – his attention, that is. He coolly sauntered over, took a sip from his banana daiquiri and made a play for the foxy chick. To his delight she reciprocated with interest and suggested they go back to his place immediately.

The stud awoke next morning still exhausted from their wild night of passionate abandon. Something weighed heavily on his chest – certainly not guilt. It was an ordinary house brick. Odd, but without a second's thought he picked it up and tossed it out of the open window.

As it sailed through the air a small handwritten note fluttered into his grasp. It read, 'Your right bollock is tied to this brick . . .' Instantly, the bloke leaped up to grab the plummeting brick. It was then he came across the second note, attached to the window frame: '. . . and your left bollock is tied to the bedpost.'

> A very visual but fundamentally flawed story, that one: why didn't he just grab a tight hold of the cord to which the brick was attached? Like I did. Whoops!

lady *luck*

A bloke of 30, yet to lose his cherry, consulted his best friend over how he could pop his cork for the first time. His mate mulled over the best means: prostitute? – nah, his pal was too sensitive a soul for that; lend him his own wife? – she'd never agree, hated the bloke. Then he remembered a woman he'd been told was free and easy with her affections: a 'sure thing'. It was decided that a blind date should be arranged, and this was duly done.

Naturally, the 'quarry' was nervous on his date, but had to put that behind him when he stopped off on the way at the chemist, just before it closed, for a packet of rubber johnnies. Mustering all the bravado available, he trousered up to the counter and blurted, 'Better give me a 12-pack, I'm feeling lucky.' The attractive young assistant smiled coyly, and the bloke rushed out as quickly as he could.

A short time later, the optimistic bloke was sitting in the chosen restaurant, clutching a bunch of flowers and a folded newspaper as arranged. A few minutes later, his blind date turned up. To the pair's mutual embarrassment she was the young woman who'd served him in the chemist, and it was quite obvious to her what he was after . . .

hamming *it up*

A well-known practice among gay men in Los Angeles – and some Hollywood actors, it's said – of slipping a hamster or gerbil up their partners' back passages (this apparently provides a highly pleasurable stimulation while the rodent scurries about) took a violent twist once when two loving partners tried it.

One bloke introduced the hamster into his mate's orifice, and awaited the moment when the ecstasy would become too much and he would have to retrieve the burrowing creature.

When this moment arrived, the bloke held up a piece of cheese to lure the hamster back out. But it wouldn't emerge, and the 'host' was in real pain. Panicking a little, his partner, who looked through the love door but couldn't see Hammy, racked his brain for a solution.

All at once he had an idea, and fumbled around for some matches. Then he lit one of them and held it close to the other bloke's bottom, hoping to shed some light on the situation and locate the errant rodent.

But by chance there was a build-up of gastric gases inside the 'host', and these were ignited by the flame. In a flash, the hamster was discharged from between the bloke's buttocks like a bullet from a blunderbuss, hitting the astonished partner full in the face and breaking his nose in two places.

For another passage to injury, read on . . .

dog*ged*

Two young lovers from Grantham were planning their marriage at their local one night when an awful realisation dawned on them. Even with the generosity of both sets of parents, there was a shortfall in their budget which meant they had to concede some of the trappings of the perfect wedding.

Among the money-saving measures they agreed was that they would ask the groom's father's next-door neighbour – a middle-aged bloke who'd recently become a widower – if they could borrow his camcorder. The neighbour readily consented and wished them all the best.

The big day was magical, and everything went swimmingly. The bride and groom were waved off from the reception and on to their hotel for the night and the prospect of nuptial delights.

The next day, the newly-weds met up with all their mates at the local pub as arranged. Naturally, they brought with them the wedding video, as yet uncut, and the landlord agreed to play it in the bar. (There was only the usual Manchester United six-nil victory finishing on Sky, so no one minded at all.)

Everyone agreed it was marvellous to see the celebrations again, and the bar fell into animated conversation as the wedding sequences finished. But then the big-screen TV was suddenly filled with what was originally on the tape. And what a surprise: there on the screen was the man who'd lent the camcorder, quite clearly shagging his pet dog.

That one, believe it or not, actually happened in Sussex, so we've included it in an attempt to redraw the bestiality map of Great Britain. The next myth is a genuine classic from the vaults of Auntie Beeb's malicious, gossiping staff. Whether it's jealousy at the inflated fees paid to their highly paid on-camera pals, or whether it's just a sort of public school mischief-making, BBC employees do seem to produce a large portfolio of unsubstantiated stories. Press any of the workforce, mind, and they'll tell you that every Christmas the engineers distribute a tape of cock-ups and pranks, though they haven't, er, actually, er, seen it themselves. Witness the Chris Evans fiasco, where the rumour mill at the BBC produced a story that secret cameras from *Noel's House Party* had accidentally caught the lanky, Channel 4 star pleasuring himself while watching *Baywatch*. Evans subsequently offered £100,000 reward to anyone who could produce the alleged recording. Like this next story, it was a classic slice of BBC bunkum.

beeb ***boob***

The BBC once had a woman newsreader, well-liked by the public but the butt of many back-handed comments from crew and backroom staff over her penchant for picking up young men after OBs (outside broadcasts).

She was the model professional on screen but, especially in her early days, like an unbridled mare on heat as soon as the red lights went out. When a story took her away from home and into hotel land, with all its possibilities, she was bound to pick up some local lad for a good rooting.

On one occasion, the crew decided to set her up. They were shooting in Manchester until late, and the filming went well. That evening, the crew waited until the presenter nipped out on the prowl as expected, and then wired up her hotel room, trailing the microphone leads into an adjoining room, where the recorder was positioned.

Sure enough, cometh the late hour, cometh the young man. The sound engineer in the adjoining room picked up the sound of the door shutting and then two voices. The lovers got down to business almost immediately, and the crew next door were creasing up at what they heard.

Nothing, however, prepared them for the memorably unguarded remarks of this household name while in a state of complete abandon. At a crucial moment in the love throes she was heard to shout, 'Fuck me, fuck me, fuck me till I fart!'

> Quite seriously, we have heard that story associated with three different women newsreaders – some more plausible than others, if you get our drift, but none verifiable . . . no matter what BBC people say to the contrary.

tyne & *weird*

The Town Moor in Newcastle upon Tyne is apparently one of the few areas, near the centre of a British city, where a commoner can give his cow a runaround. (Buckingham Palace is obviously another.)

The nuances of the by-law were clearly lost on one Geordie lad. One evening after a skinful down the notorious Bigg Market, while stumbling drunkenly across from

Spital Tongues (we kid ye not) in the west end to Jesmond out east, the T-shirted fellow was inexorably drawn towards one of the grazing cattle and, finding a nearby litter bin, placed it at the rear of the animal, dropped his trousers and began servicing the poor cow, which chewed the cud throughout.

But things suddenly went awry. Evidently, the act of bestiality was creating something of a vacuum within the cow (gases and all that) and, after a few minutes, the suction was such that the young man ceased activity.

Alarmingly, though, he wasn't able to remove his threatened member, and he began to believe he might be relieved of it if the vacuum's intensity kept increasing.

And increase it did. The power of the suction was such that the animal-lover's intestines began to be slither through his todger. Just then, luckily for him, the police found him. They tickled the cow's nose, and when it sneezed the vacuum was broken.

ring of ***confidence II***

A student nurse in Cardiff was privy to one of those moments every hospital intern dreams about, when a sexually distressed man was brought in one evening and she was deputed to treat him.

The bloke had heard that penile rings extend an erection and enhance the orgasm. But too stingy and impatient to shell out on a proper jobbie advertised in the back of the *Sunday Mirror*, he had simply removed the keys from his galvanised steel key ring and squeezed it down the shaft of his organ of pleasure. Well, in principle it worked. He summoned a huge stonker that lasted for hours. But he began to worry when, after fourteen hours without a droop, his pride and joy began to change hue from purple to black – clearly the ring restriction meant the blood wasn't circulating and he was genuinely fearful his appendage might drop off.

It was at this stage, and in a state of panic, that the nurse encountered him and his tumescent manhood. Naturally, to give all her pals a good gander, she pretended to ask their opinion on the diagnosis and called them in. The bloke was now in such pain from his incandescent inflation that he didn't care, he just wanted his makeshift dong ring taken off.

The nurse explained that none of the surgical saws they had available would suffice, and that they were waiting for a special skin-sensitive saw to arrive, the sort used by firefighters to cut away crash helmets and metal from around road traffic accident victims.

But a mean prank by one of the porters gave the poor casualty the shock of his life. The trickster rummaged around in the hospital garden shed and found what he wanted. Then he suddenly burst into the bloke's private room and sparked up a chainsaw, shouting 'Here's Willy!'

corporal *punishment*

For some years it had been the habit of squaddies stationed at Huntingdon barracks to make a stop-off on their way back to camp after a Saturday night skinful. The regular port of call was a chemist's shop letter box, through which they would prod their percies and urinate several pints of recycled Best.

The chemist was understandably aggrieved, and determined to teach the soldiers a lesson they wouldn't learn on the parade ground.

Checking his watch, the pharmacist stationed himself just inside the doorway as the pubs shut. Sure enough, a bunch of squaddies rolled round the corner and headed for the chemist's as usual.

When the first one chuckled and thrust his todger through the slot, the chemist was ready with his sharp tweezers to inflict an alarming injury. Worse still, the soldier's hasty retreat from the sharp, spring-loaded letter box meant the flap bit off more than even a Thai pleasure girl could chew, and that's a lot, apparently.

survival *stakes*

A survivalist was despised by his fellow freaks, partly because he was such a feeble-looking and creepy wretch, but mostly because whenever they went out on one of their weird survivalist weekends, he always arrived back from the wilderness at the allotted spot ahead of his rivals and in incredibly good spirits.

They all wondered what his secret was. Close scrutiny appeared to show he stuck to the rules: face smeared in camouflage colours; bandanna round head as per 'Sly' Stallone; no rudiments of civilisation carried apart from a big Bowie knife or a blanket; inane grimace; collection of brutal surgical operation photos; lunatic, masochistic dedication to self-deprivation; and a signed photograph of Oliver North, etc.

But the ease of his 'surviving' remained suspicious, and one day in the wilds another of the nutters decided to spy on him. As night drew in, the muscle-bound spy saw his quarry click flint stones together to set off kindling and make a fire, on which he boiled up grass and grubs to make a delicious and nutritious soup. Nothing unusual there, then. And as the bloke prepared for bed and appeared to reach for his swollen member, the snooper accepted that this too was normal practice for lonely survivalists.

Then the onlooker surprisingly observed that the bloke wasn't playing with himself but was appearing to dispense 10-pence coins from his foreskin like a bus conductor (from his coin machine, stupid) until he had about a quid. After that he picked up his things and strolled off, still being trailed, to the nearest phone box, where he rang and waited for a mini cab, then returned to civilisation.

> For more 'all skin and no sausage' nonsense, bivuoac in a bookshop and track down *The Return of Urban Myths*, our second best-selling batch of bull.

takes one *to know one*

A Middlesbrough lass, not known for her scintillating good looks, had arrived at the threshold of 40 without troubling the registrar's office. As it happens, her nervousness with the opposite sex had left her untouched by male hands.

Naturally, cruel as people are, there were numerous comments about this, along the lines of 'Poor old so-and-so, she cannat gerra lad' and 'Mind, I wivvent touch her with your'n!' – which is unusual for Cleveland fathers to say about their daughters. Such is life.

One day the lass returned home from a few days away with a sweet, baby-faced lad on her arm. He'd swept her off her feet and within days they were married and had set up home in Long Benton (which is what, the rumours said, he was equipped with) in Newcastle.

Everyone was canny pleased for them. After a few months of marital bliss, however, the woman was heart-broken. Imagine her shock when it was announced in the paper that 'the busies' had finally tracked down a notorious female felon, and it turned out to be her husband that the coppers had slapped the bracelets on!

The pitifully naive woman hadn't suspected a thing as her spouse had always insisted on extinguishing the lights whenever they made love.

on your *marks*

A group of lads from Leicester were on holiday in Hamburg, and wobbled into a bar in the early hours of the morning. Sitting at the bar was a buxom *fraülein* in a T-shirt bearing the challenge: 'Dump in my mouth, win 100 marks'. This was the sort of challenge the blokes adored, and within minutes the young woman was laying supine on the bar with a bare-buttocked Leicester lad's behind puckering over her face.

But just as he was about to drop his load into her open mouth, the woman blew between his buttocks. The effect on the sphincter muscles of a gust of wind like that is reflex: the muscles contracted and he was unable to defecate. One hundred marks were duly handed over, but the lads avowed to return to what was clearly an upmarket hostelry and wreak their revenge.

Three days later, one of them having consumed every bowel-loosening comestible known to man, they returned.

In deference to readers' sensibilities (yes, OK, this *is* unusual . . .) we won't recount the full details of what happened. Let's just say the blowing wasn't sufficient to staunch the flow, and the ecstatic lads won back their wager.

greek *myth*

A young lad, one of North London's Cypriot princes, was as unworldly as they come. Mollycoddled and rarely let out of the house he still shared with his prim and upright parents, he was keen to take advantage when the folks announced they were flying back to Limassol for a holiday for the first time in ages.

As soon as he'd waved them off, he went crazy. He'd never ever smoked, been drunk or had sex, so he went out and bought a packet of cigarettes, a bottle of whisky and, well, a raunchy, top-shelf video to raise the dead (till now).

Half an hour later he was prancing around the living room naked, an extra-tar fag in his mouth, slurping the hard stuff from a glass in one hand, and holding his excited John Thomas in the other, watching a hardcore porn film at top volume and in slow motion.

In a wicked twist of fate, that was how his parents, who returned home unexpectedly having forgotten their passports, discovered the son they were so proud of.

> Don't you think masturbation is a bit like voting Conservative? They all do it, but no one owns up to it.

sucker *punch*

Enjoying the X-rated Euro Disney that is Bangkok, a fashion controller from a leading men's outfitters took the inevitable step of going with one of the prostitutes displaying their wares in various seedy bars.

As the bright lights faded away, she led him to her small apartment on the outskirts of town and, business-like, immediately took him into her boudoir, where she kitted off. With her client fumbling to remove his clothes as well, and visibly excited, she whispered in his ear, 'My nipples are my speciality.' (Odd echoes of the lady of the night, a famous author and a suitcase full of readies there.)

Broadly getting her drift, the bloke fell upon her breasts like a hungry new-born baby . . . And the next thing he knew, he was lying in a strange gutter with a murderous headache, wearing nothing but a wince and robbed of all valuables.

Finding his way to a local commissariat, the Englishman – with a palm leaf strategically placed to preserve his dignity – requested help. The police officers couldn't care less. They'd seen it all before, and said there was no way he'd retrieve his belongings. All they offered him was a prison uniform to go back to his hotel in, and the smart advice to steer clear of Thai trollops' tits – nearly all of them coat their nipples with tranquillisers.

> What with the 'stolen kidney' and other unconscious sex stories, the male of the species is clearly concerned about the prospect of being given knockout drops whenever on the job. No such tranquilliser is required for some women – the

bloke's performance is normally enough to send them to sleep.

a suspect *device*

In the mid–1970s one of my uncle's pigeon-fancier mates who worked on the post was emptying his sack in the sorting office. It was during the time of the IRA letter-bombing campaign and all postal workers had been warned to be on the lookout for suspicious packages.

The vigilant postie shuffled through the letters half-asleep as usual, but then something caught his attention, making the hair stand up on the back of his neck.

It was definitely a suspect package. You couldn't get more suspect if you tried. The parcel was not only buzzing disconcertingly but it was wobbling about in an alarming fashion. It looked ready to go off at any second.

The sorting office emptied in a jiffy. People said they'd never seen post operatives move so fast without a bicycle. The police were soon on the case and cordoned off the area.

Inside, the two army bomb disposal squaddies crept nervously towards the humming parcel. Perspiring profusely, the grizzled sergeant gingerly peeled back the plain brown wrappings – only to reveal a large pulsating vibrator that had turned itself on in the post.

The name and address on the parcel was never revealed, in order to preserve the dignity of Mrs Pike of 33 Lodge Drive, Littlehampton.

the bishop's *wife*

A friend was well acquainted with the daughters of an eminent and popular bishop who sadly passed away a few years before his wife. Now she too has gone to join him beyond the pearly gates.

In his youth the bishop had answered a calling to the Far East and spent many of his formative years in the post of missionary. His wife had accompanied him there and together they spent many happy years in missionary positions throughout the Orient.

During this time the bishop's worthy wife was presented with a striking bronze medallion heavily decorated with mysterious Chinese characters and complete with chain. The cleric's spouse was so taken with the medallion that she wore it always and noted with considerable satisfaction the fascination it never failed to arouse in company. Strangely, the ornament seemed to open all kinds of doors; people seemed to want to get close to her. She put this down to the medal's talismanic effect which evinced a studied awe from Eastern intellectuals.

Despite this obvious and knowledgeable interest she never managed to have the medal's curious inscription adequately deciphered. Scholars she questioned always claimed to be unfamiliar with the nuances of that particular Cantonese dialect.

But now she'd popped her clogs and her daughters held no such love for their departed mother's prize possession. The medallion was up for auction with her other belongings. But it seemed even now to have the power to intrigue, and was definitely the most talked about item in the auction.

Not surprisingly, really: the catalogue entry read 'Three-inch-diameter solid bronze Chinese medallion. Early twentieth century Cantonese inscription reads (transl.) 'City of Shanghai Registered Prostitute No. 179'.

> Very similar in conclusion to the tale related in *The Return of Urban Myths* concerning an acupuncturist with authentic Chinese certificates, one of which turns out to be a licence to sell fish in Hong Kong harbour.

peek *charge*

In the days before Bow Street courts closed down, a streetwalker was up before the beak. The accused prostitute was charged with soliciting (have solicitors ever been charged with prostituting?) and pleaded guilty with a look of total apathy on her face.

The magistrate, a kindly old soul pledged to giving people a second chance, heard the evidence and was forced to find her guilty. But he took pity on the young girl and asked if she would like time to pay the fine – £40.

'Yer,' replied the minx to the surprised court. 'About half an hour should do it.'

> And that was in 1985. She must have been very good.

unable *seaman*

A schoolmate's dad used to be an engineer in the Merchant Navy and remembered the time his ship had docked in Marseilles.

The crew had been at sea for a couple of months and hadn't clapped eyes (or anything else) on a woman since leaving Liverpool. Understandably some of the crew were somewhat frustrated, and most of them were simply gagging for it. So as soon as the gangplank hit the dock, the sex-starved tars headed for the red light district. Luckily they didn't have too far to hobble as it was thoughtfully located very close to the docks.

One particularly repressed hornblower dashed into the first place he saw, slapped his wad – and some money – on the counter, and demanded the best in the house. The management were happy to accommodate him but he insisted on one of the women. So they led him down a dimly lit corridor to a door illuminated with strange characters. Inside candles burned and there was an intoxicating whiff of incense. Draped across the bed was most beautiful woman he had ever seen. She was tall, dark, of Oriental extraction and swathed in diaphanous silks.

The sailor gulped. He couldn't believe his luck. He puffed out his chest, strode manfully toward the vision and made to embrace her. But she evaded his clinch and stood beckoning at the corner of the bed. He lunged again, but once more she skipped free. She was obviously playing hard to get, so the sailor leapt up and set off after her.

Round and round the bed she ran with the seadog in hot pursuit, almost tripping over his tongue. He was soon getting tired of this game, but on and on she ran, twisting and turning, evading his flailing arms until he collapsed. Too exhausted to move on the bed, his heart danced a hornpipe on his ribs.

When he woke up the woman was gone and he stumbled out into the night.

The next evening the same bloke went ashore again but,

being skint, just managed to cadge enough coppers to visit a film theatre in the heart of the same district. He settled down in the plush fleapit and watched the French titles roll. From the first scene the audience was in fits. But for the seafarer the film had a spooky familiarity about it: he recognised the sad lead character vainly chasing a beautiful woman round in circles as himself – and knew exactly what *wasn't* coming next.

what a *let down*

Another merchant seaman, probably on the same ship, was away from his fiancée on a three-month stint, but took meticulous precautions against his own weak will regarding potential temptations of the flesh.

Before embarkation he purchased an inflatable doll which he kept in his sea chest in case of emergencies. But despite his preparations, when he returned to port he was forced to visit the doctors with an appalling itch. Thinking it was simply chafing from his pneumatic escapades he was shocked to hear that he had a virulent dose of the clap.

Apparently his rubber lover had been accommodating other saucy salts, one of whom who was far less fussy about his other liaisons.

That's what he told his furious ex-girlfriend, anyway.

trouser *snake'n'vac*

Obviously every nurse and hospital porter has his or her story of a late night kerfuffle, and a friend working in Birmingham still winces at the thought of one night when things were quite quiet and suddenly a fellow was brought in on a stretcher with a huge sheet draped over the middle of his body.

Naturally the staff's morbid curiosity, er, I mean, compassion, was aroused and they approached the patient one by one to see what they could glean, er, do to help.

The bloke had nearly bled to death and the reason was clear. They'd brought him in with a sheet over him because he had a short vacuum cleaner attachment still stuck firm on the symbol of his manhood.

Or what was left of it. In a bizarre solo sexual effort, the young man had fastened the domestic appliance to his one-eyed monster and switched it on. Sadly, it was rather a new model and the efficiency of its sucking action was such that his dong was extended as far as the machine's rotor blades, and he was now half the man he used to be.

And that's why all the hoses now have clips that let air in and break the vacuum.

> Before inadequately equipped gentlemen rush out to test such a member-extending tool, they should bear in mind that sometimes the polarity has been known to suddenly reverse on such machines so the contents of the dustbag are blown back up.

> Every Casualty department in every town has its share of 'objects of desire' stories and we've certainly detailed a few in our previous books, but this tale of bumfoolery has a rather nice twist. (Not if you're the patient in question though!)

behind with *the milk*

An ex-boyfriend of a friend used to be a medical student and was working in the Casualty department of the local hospital when a fellow claiming to be a window cleaner was rushed through in obvious agony.

The poor man was face-down on the stretcher and had a milk bottle firmly wedged up his back passage.

The doctors and nurses had seen this 'rear entry' type of thing many times before and tried to keep straight faces as the window cleaner ran through his tale. Apparently he'd been up his ladder, wringing out his chamois when he'd slipped, flipped over in mid-air and landed legs akimbo on top of the empty gold top.

The sniggering staff were convinced the story was a concoction and that the bloke had been indulging in some perverse act or other.

One buttock-relaxing injection later, the empty milk bottle was removed. To everyone's astonishment it clearly contained two perfectly punched-out circles of fabric, one from the window cleaner's blue denim jeans and the other from his red nylon underpants.

And to show no gender bias . . .

fruit of *the womb*

A nurse in Melbourne was on duty in the Casualty department one night when a woman was rushed in on a stretcher with an apple stuck where the sun don't shine. Her story was intriguing. She'd been cleaning the blinds in the living room when she'd slipped and fallen spread-eagled on to a fruitbowl. The apple had become lodged, and despite all sorts of efforts to retrieve it, it remained stuck up her innards.

The medics present were nevertheless unconvinced by the mirth-inducing explanation.

'Do you often do the housework without knickers on?' asked one doctor, obviously interested merely in a professional capacity. 'And do you often keep apples in your bowl that have had a good bite taken out of them?' quizzed another.

> While on the subject of things 'stuck up' (do we ever get off it? . . .), the latest in the long line of 'Women/bloke admitted to Casualty, pains in stomach, surgery reveals . . .' tales ends in the words 'cucumber plant roots in womb/colon'. Just thought you'd like to know. We could of course show you the list of reported 'foreign bodies retrieved from various human orifices' from an article in *Surgery* magazine from 1986, but you wouldn't be interested in that, would you? Oh you would!
>
> 'Two glass tubes; a jeweller's saw; an oil can with a potato stopper(!); umbrella handle; two glasses; 402 stones; toolbox (a convict had saws, files, etc. for escape attempt); two bars of soap; beer glass and jam pot; a lemon and a cold cream jar; two apples; a whip handle; spectacles, suitcase key; tobacco pouch and a magazine (some fall!); torch; icepick; zucchini; salami; knife sharpener; frozen pig's tail; kangaroo skin tumour; mortar and pestle.'

> Easily the most common surgically-retrieved items are bottles, vibrators, broom handles, carrots, glasses (no, not spectacles) and, of course, kangaroo tumours . . . I mean, dildos. But of course there are more than two human orifices . . .

land of the *not-so-rising sun*

A working girl in London's Soho, who knows these things, asserts that Japanese businessmen always insist on having sex with the lights out.

Apparently Japanese males are so poorly endowed beneath the kimono that they are forced to wear strap-on penis extensions when they visit European prostitutes to avoid humiliation.

> There, that'll teach 'em for Pearl Harbor. Over in Texas of course they say everything's bigger – even the codswallop. Well, this next tale's certainly a whopper.

a relative *shock*

Deep in the Texas panhandle a young couple were caught camping out in an area of desert where such things are strictly forbidden. Although it was dusk the eagle-eyed Texas Rangers had spotted a flashlight and headed across country in their patrol vehicle to confront the miscreants.

The young guy heard the engine and ducked out of the canvas begging for leniency. Coming clean, he admitted they'd run away from home but were both just under-age, even though recently his voice had dropped and his balls had broken(!). The grizzled patrolmen were in a quandry about what to do when the youngster popped back in the tent and, after a hurried discussion, came up with a novel solution to the problem.

Apparently the teenage girl in the tent had offered to perform oral sex with the Rangers if they let the couple off. It had been a hard few hours on the road and the grinning cops readily agreed.

The sergeant cockily let the younger patrolman go first, to save time, so he reckoned. A few minutes later it was the sergeant's turn and, to the sound of his zipper bursting open in anticipation, he entered the tent – only to come face to face with his own daughter.

> Service in the Forces often requires an understanding lover but, as the next story suggests, an understanding lover often needs forceful service.

night *duty*

The Hampshire police were called out to a domestic in the early hours, shortly after a large naval frigate had docked in Portsmouth harbour. Four quarrelling sailors on shore leave were arrested and taken down to the cells. Each one claimed to have been visiting his girlfriend when the others had turned up all clutching identical signed photos of the same woman. A punch-up inevitably ensued.

They all swore she was a real looker and fabulous in bed. The police sergeant was desperate to see what kind of bombshell could keep four lusty seamen satisfied and demanded to see the photos. When the sailors obliged, he couldn't believe his eyes. For there, scantily clad in the briefest of frillies, was his own wife, obviously doing a night shift of her own.

a poor ***show***

A bunch of no-good lazy hard-drinking students (ah! those were the days – with Thatcher's children, forget it) set up a pirate radio station in Bath which became incredibly – one might say inconceivably – popular with listeners in the area. They were very big in the Bristol area, so to speak.

One evening in the pub, one of the top student DJs charmed the pants off a group of young women from the local nursing college. Then, taking a few carry-outs with him, of course, he invited them back to the radio station 'to see where it all happens'.

The lads were more than pleased to see their mate's guests and interviewed the nurses live on air about harrowing cases and lewd admissions to Casualty. (Shame they didn't make some admissions of their own.)

It had been a pretty good show, and they signed off and got down to serious business: drinking and chatting up the nurses. The lights may have been dimmed, but passions were ablaze and 15 minutes later the students were flaked out smoking their celebratory fags. Then the nurses started shouting out scores to each other. Not sparing the poor lads' blushes they called out each name and detailed every inadequacy in their technique.

As you can imagine, this took quite a while. The students were gobsmacked. What could possibly be more embarrassing than to have their sexual shortcomings paraded like that? Then one of them spotted something definitely more embarrassing – a little red light blinking in the dark. They were still live on air.

a ball ***bearing incident***

A well-respected Glasgow engineer, who worked in the drawing office of the shipyards, was proud of his position and kept himself apart from the lower orders as he saw them. A loner by nature, he often disappeared to the factory lav in the afternoons, with his favourite magazine hidden inside a copy of *The Scotsman* for a bit of recreation.

Being blessed with an enquiring mind he endeavoured to work out a way of maximising his pleasure. He'd tried leaning on his arm until it went dead and felt like someone else was doing it, and all the usual tricks, but he still wasn't satisfied.

Then one day, back on the shopfloor, he came across a large circular stainless steel ball race (a metal collar full of ball bearings used in engineering to cut down friction on drive shafts) with an opening of a familiar diameter (like that of the grip of his hand), and popped it in his pocket. Trousers bulging, he entered the bog at the usual time.

The ball race certainly did the trick and he soon worked himself up into quite a lather. Then disaster struck. The ball race must have been a little too tight. Unable to contain a scream he was horribly caught in the mechanism.

Minutes late, the gibbering engineer had to be embarrassingly stretchered out past his dumbfounded colleages.

> Ah, urban myths: from heavy petting to light engineering in the flick of a wrist.

flippering ***dangerous II***

A friend of a bloke in the same office took a year off and went round the world. During his time in the Pacific, he was doing some island hopping when he witnessed an astounding ritual with its beginnings shrouded in the mists of time.

Apparently the tribe indigenous to the island swim out to sea and mate with the dolphins as part of a bizarre fertility rite (don't try this one at home). The intoxicating rhythms of the pounding drums and the emotive torch-lit ritual performed at dusk got right under the skin of one brazen American tourist. Giving way to primitive yearnings, she stripped off and ran into the foaming waves desperate to join in the primeval rite.

Sadly, none of the dolphins seemed even vaguely interested in her so she swam back to the shore. Then smearing herself from head to toe in ceremonial fish paste, to make herself more attractive to marine life, she plunged back into the surf.

It worked a treat. She hadn't got very far out before she was devoured in a frenzy by sharks.

There are of course tales of flipper-lust closer to home, like the woman who ran into the sea in

Cardigan Bay shouting, 'Fungie, Fungie, I love you' to her briny beau. There's also the case of the chap from Whitley Bay who used to frolic naked with his aquatic chum but always claimed that if anything untoward did happen, it wasn't on porpoise. The next two tales should really fall into our Transports of Delight section as they've far more to do with pubic than public transport.

express *your love*

A friend regularly travels by InterCity Silver Service – like standard class but with a paper tablecloth thrown in for an extra thirty quid each way. One day she got chatting with one of the stewards she fancied and he told her about an incident which had occurred only a few days earlier on his mate's 125.

It was the midnight run down from Edinburgh to London and the train was fairly empty. One young couple who'd obviously had a bit to drink were in a semi-empty carriage, snogging furiously. They didn't even look up to have their tickets punched.

The couple's lascivious passion became more and more inflamed and, not content with heavy petting, their carnal desires ran wild and they began making mad, passionate love on the table. Blissfully engrossed in their hedonistic performance, they hammered away over the points, until they parted, exhausted, and slumped back into their seats.

Then the bloke struck a match to light a post-coital cigarette for his love. Oddly, it illuminated a lewd thong of leering faces. They'd watched the whole licentious performance in silence, but now decided to make their presence felt, tut-tutting and pointing to the 'no smoking' signs.

the bus *seductress*

Back in the swinging Sixties a paint-spattered fine-artist friend from Dunfermline was kept waiting at his bus stop for an inordinate length of time and only found out the reason the next day.

The regular bus driver on his route had recently been joined by a young clippie who he'd immediately taken a shine to. She was a fine looking young lassie and had customised her uniform to conform to the mini skirt fashion of the day. As a result the bus was always full of working men, many travelling way past their usual stops.

The driver, a young chap himself, had taken to wearing an open-necked shirt and powerful aftershave and insisted on personally showing the young clippie the ropes. She was not immune to his charms and despite his acrid cologne they soon became close friends – very close friends.

But there was an impediment to their young love. Both of them lived at home with their parents and it was hard to get time alone on their own. So they took to making the beast with two backs in the empty double-decker after the last run on a Friday night, when it became their own little passion wagon. It was just the ticket, though probably against company regulations. Their sessions also included some of the shortest rides the bus ever experienced.

One hot summer Friday evening the young driver's passions became particularly heated and as he yanked on the handbrake in the deserted garage, his love wrenched open the door and pounced on him in the cab rather than waiting for their usual back-seat tryst.

Close to the end of the line, though, they experienced a fearsome 'lovers' cramp' and became inextricably coupled.

They were still jammed together the following Monday, when they were discovered by the raucous early-morning shift who immediately phoned the sniggering Fire Brigade to cut them free.

> Perhaps it's a shame they weren't on board the number 69. What with cutting free all these love-locked couples and damping down the fires of passion (frequently exposed in our *Urban Myths* and *The Return of . . .*), it's surprising the Fire Brigade ever have the time to extinguish any real fires.

nec-*romancer*

The elderly undertaker in a small Derbyshire town had kept a secret for years. To the public he was a sombre, upright man of dignity who always keffed of formaldehyde; by night he was much more upright than they imagined, and was in the habit of acquiring carnal knowledge of the cadavers in his charge.

To his suppressed delight, one day a distraught family asked him to handle the funeral arrangements of their dearly departed 18-year-old daughter. Solemnly taking delivery of her corpse the undertaker drove, skipping red lights, back to his parlour.

As soon as he arrived, he gave his assistant the afternoon off, drew all the curtains, turned the door sign to 'closed' and jumped naked into the lovely young woman's coffin. Then he had his wicked way with her.

Midway through the necrophilic act, the late lass shockingly shot bolt upright, coughing and screeching, and clearly not very dead at all. The undertaker tried to disguise what was going on by quickly applying a screwdriver to the casket, but to no avail.

When the parents discovered what had happened, they revealed that their daughter had been in a coma after a crash and had been pronounced clinically dead – wrongly, as it proved. The shock of the funeral director's intrusion stirred her back to life, and the family were so grateful they declined to press charges against him and the whole thing was hushed up.

Sex etc.

* 'Fuckie fuckie?' is a universally understood request
* Thai prostitutes can remove bottle tops with their lips (not the facial ones)
* There's a 'Ladies Only' bar in Amsterdam that has a set of small doors in the wall. Behind each is a man's penis which can be fondled for a price
* Every now and then Napoleon's penis comes up for auction at Sotheby's
* If blokes masturbate too much in one day, only air comes out
* Not only that, but you'll be slowly jerking yourself off to the pearly gates: every ejaculation contains a high amount of essential zinc
* A cocky undergraduate annoyed a lab technician to such an extent that, during a demonstration, the technician poured half a litre of acetone down the student's trousers and froze his balls
* An unfaithful man thrown downstairs by his wife was castrated by the steel comb in his pocket
* The spread of BSE from cows to humans has been blamed on farmers servicing their animals, but the EC report proving it has been hushed up
* In olden days, women would travel to Tyburn not to see the hangings, but to check how well hung the

victims were – men killed in this manner get huge erections

* A bunch of top groupies specialise in shagging rock stars and taking plaster casts of their idols' privates – one sneaked in and did Jim Morrison while he lay on the slab

what's ***my line***

Occupational hazards

Clock on for a roll-call of downsized human resourcefulness in the face of the cut and thrust of business. The shiftless shirkers here haven't a clue concerning the job at hand. This is mass-produced mayhem at its best. Every day is pay day when the protesting work ethic is fully applied and the wages of sin are being doled out

water *tight*

A florist who works around the corner swears that her line of work is just as exciting as any other, and who are we to disagree? Take the time just before Christmas when an obese and opulent lady came into the shop to buy a festive flower arrangement, but ended up making something of a display of herself. Flower shops have to crank up the heating in winter in order to keep some of the more delicate specimens inside happy – but it's not just the staff who like warmth, some tropical blooms need it too.

Anyhow, the posh and portly female customer was suffering in the damp, muggy heat, and began to sweat and fret. Before a shop assistant could gather a chair for her to sit down on, the corpulent madame went pale and passed out, tumbling down amid some gardening equipment with a huge thump.

The staff didn't know what to do at first. The poor woman was way too portly for them to lift, so they had to revive her with smelling salts and slappings of wrists where she lay. Happily, after a minute, the woman came round and managed to sit up. And, declaring she didn't want to cause a concern, the rich dame suddenly stood up and strode out to go about her business.

However, one thing suggested that the immense dame still hadn't quite come to her senses. For as she waddled out, the staff couldn't help but notice that she had a large green watering can protruding from between her ample buttocks.

She was always spouting off anyway.

A friend of someone we spoke to on the Anne and Nick show works at the tourist office in the delightful Pennine locale of Hattersley. Apparently, this spot, popular with Yorkshire folk and normal people alike, has one of the highest ratios of 'panic buttons' per shop in the country. Naturally, the information bureau is suitably equipped.

This is perhaps just as well, for all sorts of oddballs find their way to God's own county, and many want information (like how to get out again). On the woman's first day in the office, a quaintly attired, unshaven and slightly slavering gent appeared at the counter.

'Can you tell me how many psychopaths there are in Hattersley, and where I can find them?' he asked, and it seemed to the tremulous woman he went boss-eyed a little. She pretended she didn't hear the question and asked him to repeat it.

Same question: 'How many psychopaths are there in Hattersley?'

The woman was unnerved – she'd read all those stories about care in the community for the violently deranged, and believed them – and fumbled under the desk for the panic button while professing no knowledge on the subject. 'I'm more gymkhanas and spam-frying events myself,' she stuttered.

The customer was also becoming agitated. 'Call yourself a tourist office? You don't know anything about psychopaths. Flipping pathetic!' he stormed, turning on his heel and retreating in a huff. With some relief, the woman watched him leave, and noticed something: he was wearing bicycle clips. Then it dawned on her – he'd been innocently asking her about paths specially designated for cyclists.

Which is slightly reminiscent of the elderly woman we heard about who travels to London by coach for a show, visits a pub in Hampstead and over-indulges on the *vino tinto*, leaving her brand-new duel-lensed spectacles on the bar when it's time to go. Then she suddenly remembers the goggles, bursts back into the pub and exclaims drunkenly, 'Has anyone seen my bisexuals?'

collection ***bowl***

In a cavernous church in one of the leafy districts of Birmingham, an elderly clergyman had taken to preaching God's word through a clip-on bug microphone – his voice was on the wane through too many of the Good Lord's High-Tar King-Size, and his flock had that irritating habit of not occupying the first three rows of pews.

One Sunday, addressing one of his biggest congregations for weeks (20 or 30 souls), the vintage cleric was in mid-flow, relating the story of Noah, when suddenly a faraway look flitted across his face. He instantly called his listeners to silence, asking them to kneel and bow their heads in contemplation of the Great Flood. Then he himself fell silent.

But the loudspeakers in the church began to pick up the sound of a creaking door, then a wooden lid being raised, and shortly after that the sound of holy vestments being lowered, accompanied by a sigh from the old vicar. The congregation sat in embarrassment as their holy man's grunts, an extended 'dibble-dibble' and large sporadic splashes were relayed by his still-broadcasting clip-on micro-

phone. Finally, job over, the paperwork was heard to be done, the toilet flushed and the door creaked again – all in the house of God.

Understandably, when he returned to the his pulpit, the dotty old preacher couldn't fathom why all his flock were stifling sniggers.

making the *grade*

A young Bristol woman had graduated in computer studies at university and after a few years working in various under-funded British research establishments, the young lady reluctantly joined the brain drain and emigrated to the US of A.

She found a job at a big Midwestern college, but was alarmed at some of the bizarre practices there. They came to a head at the end of her first year, when the computer students delivered their first exam papers. She was marking them along with a senior tutor, and couldn't help noticing that even if he sounded very impressed with a paper, when he passed it on to her it had been quite clearly marked with a big, fat 'Fail'. And this was the mark she had to enter into the college computer as the student's result.

Having allowed several of these apparent contradictions to pass, the young lecturer eventually plucked up the courage to query a mark. 'You kept saying how great this paper was, and then you put down a fail. Why?'

Her senior looked at her with disdain – were all Limeys this dopey? 'Look, it's standard practice here in America,' he said. 'The reason I put all of them down as a fail is that any whizz kid worthy of the name should be able to hack into our files and change their grades themselves.'

the cavity *cowboys*

A friend of a friend, a grease monkey, worked for a few weeks as a cut-price cavity wall insulation filling specialist. On their very first day, he and his incompetent mate were called out by an elderly lady in an draughty Victorian terraced house.

The pair clattered up in their hand-painted knackered old van. Then having reassured the poor dear and packed her off shopping, they set about reading the DIY book they'd brought at the market on the way to see what they should do.

The wall that needed filling was found and, grappling with a huge masonry drill, one of the team clumsily bored through until he reached the cavity. Then his partner attached the large foam canister to the injector and began to impregnate the gap.

After 15 minutes he was still pumping away. The foam in one massive drum having been consumed, the cowboys attached another canister and returned to their task. But within a short time the injecting equipment was once again spitting air.

Something was clearly going awry, but the lads carried on regardless even when the lady of the house returned. A few minutes later, though, their graft was cut short by the exasperated cursing of the old woman. They protested their innocence – what had they done to deserve this?

'Look for yourself,' screamed the woman, pounding them with a brolly and leading them into the adjoining room where she flung open the wardrobe doors.

Sadly, the cowboys had drilled a little too far, and the huge clothes cupboard was crammed to the hinges with solid, yellow, quick-dried foam.

what ***a card***

A friend of a friend is one of London's finest – a cabbie. Some years back he was driving down picturesque Whitehall when a pin-striped, respectable-looking gent frantically flagged him down and shouted that he had to be in Convent Garden *prontissimo.*

With traffic fuming on either side of his black cab, the driver explained that he'd have to drive to the end before turning round. The passenger suggested that he might perform a U-turn. The cabbie wasn't keen because it was illegal on Whitehall and, worse, the place was usually crawling with Old Bill.

'If you do a U-turn, my man, I'll make it worth your while,' oozed the gent. At the prospect of a 'big bung' the cab driver hauled on the wheel. But sure enough, just as he crossed the middle of the road a police car, siren ablaze, hauled the cab over. The coppers were dismissive of the driver's protestations and were just about to throw the book at him when the important gent in the back spoke up. 'If you have any trouble with these officers, young man, come and see me in my Chambers in the morning.' And he handed the cabbie his card.

The coppers were irritated beyond belief. The passenger was obviously a judge, JP or some other beak, and there was no way they were going to make the charges stick. Grudgingly, they allowed the happy cabbie to continue his journey to Covent Garden unmolested.

Some weeks later, the cabbie came across the card the gent had given him and for the first time studied it. It read, 'George Jones, Fruit and Veg, Covent Garden Chambers'.

making ***a splash***

A new captain was appointed to sort out one of the most unruly ships in the Queen's fleet, and immediately set about improving discipline. But he was a decent fellow and quite fair about how he achieved his aims.

Take the night the crew returned from an evening's debauchery in a tropical Caribbean port – the whole town, in fact, was awash with seamen (it took them days to clean up afterwards). The skipper straddled the top of the gangplank and stopped the sozzled tars with a view to stifling their after-hours drinking.

The first few mariners arrived and their superior subtly reminded them of the alcohol ban, just in case they happened to be trying to bring some on board. Then he gave them the chance to avoid being slapped in the brig, by turning his back and coughing so the sailors might throw away any contraband bottles. Three splashes over the side satisfied him that the chaps had dutifully unburdened themselves, and he waved them on.

Some time later, another couple of salty seadogs teetered shipward, and the captain assumed the position once more, blocking off their hammock access. Clearly these two steamers were the type who loved a tot o' rum, and they were bound to be secreting a bottle or two about their persons to pursue their inebriation. As before he alluded to the fact that his was a 'dry' ship, and suggested there might be something the seamen would like to throw overboard, then he turned his back discreetly.

The wily old tars, plastered as they were, soon provided the skipper with the two splashes he was waiting for. With a satisfied smile, the captain swivelled round to wave the men on board. But as he did so, he happened to glance down at their feet – and saw with some annoyance that each of them had a shoe missing.

miner *inconvenience*

The strapping son of a friend's uncle from Nottinghamshire had worked down the pit ever since he left school (at seven). So he was used to the problem when he was caught short one mile down with, shall we say, limited (i.e. non-existent) toilet facilities.

He simply sought out a quiet corner away from the seam, slipped down his hooded overalls and assumed the position for number twos.

A few grunting minutes later, the bloke had finished his underground log and decided to head back to the coalface. So he swiftly slipped his arms back in the sleeves, wrenched the overalls back on and quickly pulled up his hood, only to feel a heavy, damp splat on the back of his neck . . .

> A similar scatalogical escapade springs to mind, concerning a soldier caught short in his chemical warfare get-up inside a tank during a nuclear conditions war game, who got a rather nasty pat on the neck in front of his commanding officer . . . Luckily they all had gas masks inside the tank.

skid *marks*

In the Italian alpine resort of Bardonecchia, during the 1970s, there lived and worked a monstrously conceited ski instructor. He was a real Gio Cool medallion man: permanent tan, cool wrap-around shades, footballer's perm – the full set. And he was God's gift to women, naturally, especially *après* the *après-ski* in the open-fired wooden chalets.

But during one season, he'd been going through a bit of a lean spell with the ladies and his confidence was at a low ebb. Worse, he was approaching the big 4–0 but, still hot to trot, he fancied his chances at the slightest glint in a woman's eye, and on one occasion he had a class of giggling novices who all happened to be female.

Dusting off all the usual moves – wrapping his arms around the foxy chicks to show how to hold the sticks, standing behind them on the skis and wiggling their hips with his – he was feeling really good and moving in for the kill. He wasn't fussy about which quarry he had later.

However, he had a weight on his mind and on his digestive system. It must have been the five helpings of curried Gouda fondue the night before. He knew he couldn't wait, he had to go on the piste.

Involving the lovely ladies in a practice manoeuvre, he boasted that he had to collect something important from someone he'd just seen ski past, then streaked away behind some bushes close by. Then dropping his slinky Lycra ski pants, he let go in haste. As soon as he'd completed the exercise, he took a deep breath and slalomed back to his gaggle of learners, beaming as if nothing had happened.

But something had happened, and from the sniggers of the young women it was clear they knew what it was. The bloke was mortified. How could they possibly know. He'd been so discreet about it.

Then as he followed their tittering stares, it was suddenly staring him in the face. The bottom had fallen out of his world and the evidence was clear to see, still steaming on the end of his skis.

supply *and demand*

During the Gulf War, supply ships were the life-line of the fleet. Not just for the obvious reasons – ammo, food, etc. – but also for the officer's libidos, as wives were sometimes allowed to travel on the non-combatant vessels.

It was the practice on one ship for the wives and female members of the crew to take advantage of the warm weather around the Tropic of Cancer by lying out on the deck during quiet moments. One day the male crew of a gunship moored nearby decided to spy on the scantily-clad women as they sunbathed. This was possible by disconnecting the hi-tech sights of the big guns from the centralised, computerised weapons system and using them as incredibly efficient peeping-tom bins.

For a few minutes the ogling lads enjoyed an eyeful of officer class totty. But then a furious officer stormed on to the deck and, red-faced with rage, demanded to know what was going on – the soppy sailors had neglected to disconnect the sights from the guns and all the ship's big guns were trained on to the supply vessel where their senior officers and wives were catching the rays.

punch *lines*

A feeble geography teacher in Stroud was frequently the victim of the subtle wit of one of the most mischievous kids in the school, and driven to distraction in the process. Other teachers were equally exasperated and dished out punishment daily for the errant lad to deliver – 500 lines was the common censure – but the chronic backlog of lines was often their undoing.

The cocky lad seemed immune to such measures and

never seemed to do them. Whenever the geography master was pushed to the brink, he would scream at the boy, 'Right! 300 lines: "I must not gesticulate, prevaricate or provide distraction in geography".' At which point the insolent youth would whip out a diary and reply: 'I'm so booked up with lines, sir, the earliest I can fit you in is next April – is that OK?'

red-hot *sermon*

A woman at college remembers hearing about a strange occurrence at a friends' local church during the Good Friday Mass. Easter is a very special time in Catholic countries and in many respects takes precedence over Christmas as the premier festival of the religious calendar. The little village deep in the heart of Normandy was no exception to religious devotion and the place of worship was packed to the rafters with pious parishioners. The priest was very pleased to see such a full house and his breast swelled with pride as he gazed out upon the expectant faces of his flock. Tier upon tier of candles gave an ethereal luminescence to the solemn proceedings, their reflected light shimmering from the heavily gilded frescoes and embracing the huge stone-encrusted golden crucifix in their honeyed glow.

Suffused with emotion, the priest began his reverie, swaying back and forth reciting his mantra. As he reached the crescendo of his eulogy he noticed the congregation becoming carried away by the spirit of the occasion, and many were on their feet. Some even seemed to be calling out and with their arms raised, behaviour more appropriate to a Baptist revival meeting, he considered, but he was filled with an inner warmth that his flock had been so ignited by passion. The altar itself seemed to have become a radiant beacon of light that was glowing brighter and brighter.

Sadly, the spell was broken when the congregation threw him to the floor, rolled him in an altar rug and stamped out his blazing cassock. He might not have ignited their religious fervour but he'd done a pretty good job on his robes with the altar candles.

the ***bridge***

A few years back a friend studying at Brunel University was lucky enough to grab a seat in a packed lecture hall to hear an address given by an eminent professor to the University's Engineering Society. The don was delivering an oration on the subject of unusual railway bridges, so as you would expect the hall was full to bursting with budding engineers and their peers. The learned professor cut a fine figure at the lectern and, well practised in the art of public speaking, punctuated his talk with pithy comment and slides of the breathtaking constructions. His knowledge seemed to know no bounds, he knew the subject inside out.

He singled out many interesting and innovative designs for praise, dropping names like 'aiches' at a cockney knees-up, then turned on one particular unusual example and slated it. He criticised the titanic structure's site, the design, the construction methods and its environmental impact. Did he not like that bridge.

When the applause had died down, there was a question and answer session. An elderly gentleman raised his hand

and, returning to the subject of the maligned bridge, took some time to explain the reasons, as he understood them, for the unusual nature of the bridge's aspect and fabrication.

The professor, his feathers ruffled by this contentious interruption and feeling the limelight slipping away, puffed out his chest and pointedly put the old fellow down for audaciously implying that he knew more about this subject than he did himself.

'Well, I should,' replied the studious old fellow. 'You see, I designed and built that particular bridge myself.'

> The uses and abuses of the Registered Mail Service have been well documented in *The Return of Urban Myths*. But this next yarn angling for your attention is definitely a bit fishy.

fin *mail*

The Royal Mail have a special complaints and missing letters department to deal with any mishaps. A friend of a friend from Durham used to work in the North Eastern office and had to deal with a curious call. A customer claimed that a side of smoked salmon posted to her a few days earlier had not been delivered.

She had proof of posting and all the requisite paperwork was in order, but it seemed the salmon had vanished. So the Post Office happily paid compensation for the loss and forgot all about the affair.

A few steaming hot summer months later the woman rang the office to let them know she had found the missing fish. It appeared the postman had indeed dutifully delivered the long thin parcel through the letter box, but it had slithered across the highly polished floor and skidded under the hall dresser. Then it had remained, concealed from sight but sadly not from smell, as the poor woman was only to ready to testify.

She was keen to send it in as proof, but her offer was firmly but politely declined.

> A friend's dad was an old sea dog with 25 years' service in the Royal Navy to his credit, and during his time afloat he heard many tales of selfless heroism in the heat of battle and heart-stopping yarns of derring-do, as well as the ones related here.

a cobbler's ***dream***

Apparently one of the old tar's shipmates was quite tall. In fact he was very tall, enormous, even; 6 feet 9 inches in his stockinged feet. His other appendages were obviously of the same gargantuan proportions, so it goes without saying that his feet were colossal.

The giant seafarer could only just fit into size 18 boots which had to be tailor-made, or cobbler-made. The oversize plates led to a few problems on board ship. His insoles were as big as some people's arseholes. The bloke's shoes were so huge it meant he couldn't turn round in narrow corridors. He had to go to the end of the sometimes very long passageways in order to change direction. Which must have given him the perfect excuse for being late.

At least that ship would never be short of lifeboats in an emergency.

terminal ***trouble***

Another salt also claimed to have problems with his feet. The mariner had been back late from a heavy night's carousing on shore and was being carpeted by the furious Captain.

'Where the dickens have you been until this ungodly hour?' he bawled.

'Well, sir,' came the reply. 'I was hurrying back to the ship well on time, when I got my boot stuck in a tram line and had to walk all the way back to the terminus to get it free.'

to cap ***it all***

Yet another Navy man was back on board late – in fact, so late that it was the morning after the night before when he eventually made it back to ship. The chief was apoplectic, spitting with rage, and demanded a full explanation. He warned his subordinate that he'd be on a charge – and a highly explosive one at that.

The unable seaman dolefully ran through the night's events and conceded he'd been very much the worse for drink. So much the worse that he'd lost his cap – and without the name on the cap, he couldn't remember which ship he was on.

shelf-help *scheme*

The local library was moving to the other side of town and, as ever in these times, due to central government prioritising funds to line the pockets of their friends in the City, money was tight for the thriving public service.

But then the chief librarian had a rare brainwave to cut down on transportation costs and encourage increased use by the community. The library encouraged every one of their borrowers to take out ten books each for an extended period – six weeks.

The books were duly returned after the library had moved to its new site, thereby saving a fortune in removal costs.

> While on the subject of libraries, one of the authors (the whispering one) used to work in such an establishment in Hornsey, North London. Among the motley collection of clients there was a woman who used to claim the Russians were coming and that therefore the photocopier wouldn't work (in reality the repairer wasn't coming, which was why the photocopier didn't work), and a man – allegedly a former top-ranking university don – who would rant around the bookshelves, work his way into the reading room, open up the *Daily Mail* and via quick-release trousers that facilitated an easy dump, drop waste on to the centre pages. Always the *Daily Mail* . . . What taste.

badly *stitched up*

A chirpy cockney fisherman who ran a fleet of small boats out of Walton-on-the-Naze made his stash and retired far away in Frinton. As a memento of his life-long occupation and to celebrate the source of his prosperity – jellied eels – he had a fetching wallet fashioned solely from eelskin.

Sadly, the first time he used the new billfold, all his credit cards were wiped clean and he became a pauper overnight. It's a little known fact that eels can drastically affect plastic money – so make a note never to buy an eelskin wallet even if it's going cheap.

that sinking *feeling*

A renowned architect was commissioned by an even better-known university to create a centrepiece to its sporting facilities, a state-of-the-art Olympic swimming pool which its overseas and sporting scholarship students could use to train for major international events. It would bring prestige, and, no doubt, more lucrative overseas students to study at the university.

The architect's meticulous plans and space-age innovative design wowed the assembled dons at the first meeting and they excitedly rubber-stamped his proposals, looking forward to profile-boosting media interest and the big-time nosh at the grand opening ceremony.

The months flew by, and the project was fulfilled. A minor royal, pushing his talents to the limits, snipped the ribbon at the unveiling and everyone piled into the top-drawer buffet.

But a few months after the inauguration the professors were stressed, as was the swimming pool: cracks were appearing everywhere and the pool building was already half a metre beneath its original level.

It seems the soppy big-name architect had slightly miscalculated the weight of water in the swimming pool and the baths were sinking fast.

> Something of a minor classic, that one. The same oversight is also levelled at building designers who plan libraries but don't allow for the weight of the books – they're virtually solid tree trunks when stacked on a shelf. Talking of which, why has it taken so long for the new British Library to open?

snakes *alive*

A film director who works out of darkest Soho heard about a shoot that didn't quite go according to the storyboard. The crew in question were shooting a commercial for something or other and the day was going well, the client was with the ad team happily ensconced in the exotic wine bar across the road, being entertained by a number of friendly hostesses, and they were well ahead of their shooting schedule.

The experienced team, from one of the top London agencies, had worked long and hard to come up with an unparalleled visual feast, but as usual had plumped for a half-naked woman and a pack shot instead.

The crew excitedly set up the rig to do the next scene, which involved a lissom black model in a micro bikini draped over some animal skins and a large python – all in the best possible taste.

The snake was required to slither erotically across the young woman's naked stomach to emphasise some unique selling proposition about the product.

The director licked his lips; everything was ready: the lighting was suitably seductive, the woman looked fantastic and the snake and his trainer were ready for action.

But after take 26 the director was getting a little frazzled, the snake just wouldn't perform. It was simple enough, just a quick slither across the woman's abdomen, then off. But the creature dried, refused to cooperate and the trainer couldn't do a thing with him. The director was at the end of his tether when he remembered a trick from a wildlife documentary he'd seen, and bundled the snake into the mini-bar.

The drowsy reptile was released from the fridge half an hour later and the assistant director told to superglue a piece of fishing wire to the serpent's nose, in order to drag it across the women's belly whether it liked it or not.

The assistant director was not altogether comfortable with snakes, and made a terrible mistake. He found in his panic that he'd glued his finger fast to the poisonous hissing reptile's nose, just as it started to wake up under the hot studio lights . . .

Top jobs

* Two male ministers in the British government are well-known lovers. The Prime Minister banned them from sitting next to each other at cabinet meetings because they used to hold hands
* A former minister, now living in Europe, used to take taxis from Westminster to Harwich most Thursdays so he could voyage to Scandinavia where his paedophilic proclivities were fully catered for
* After MP Stephen Milligan's death by auto-asphyxiation, everyone knew of a local bishop who suffered the same fate but it was all hushed up – particularly in Hampstead
* During the Cold War before 'glasnost', KGB agents would scour dustbins in Knightsbridge looking for state secrets
* The Queen has terminal cancer and a colostomy bag (of course she hasn't) and it's all been hushed up
* Junior officers in the Royal Marines have a punishment for uppity colleagues they'd like to quit the force: ordeal by mud. The brown stuff is crammed into every orifice of the victim. Just ask Prince Edward
* Mary Queen of Scots held a coherent conversation for fifteen minutes after her head was chopped off, a record for the royal family

wan*ted*

As part of our mission to collate all the world's greatest urban myths, we invite readers who would like to share their best stories with us to write them down and kindly send them to:

Phil Healey and Rick Glanvill
Planet X
97 St John Street
London EC1M 4AS

We are particularly interested in aprocryphal stories connected with occupations like the emergency services, the armed forces and social work, and in urban legends from around the globe, but all contributions are much appreciated.

Details of other Virgin humour titles appear on the following pages

URBAN MYTHS

Phil Healey and Rick Glanvill

This hilarious collection of contemporary 'true stories' unleashes over 200 new, borrowed and blue urban myths, starring the ubiquitous 'friend-of-a-friend'. They're saucy, implausible, bizarre and sometimes scary – and as with all the best yarns, they have a spooky ring of truth. In a society obsessed by gossip, URBAN MYTHS are the best unfounded stories around. Read them here and never trust that, 'No, but it really happened' line again.

ISBN 0 86369 686 4

THE RETURN OF URBAN MYTHS

Phil Healey and Rick Glanvill

More incredible but 'true' stories of sex, drink and unreliable machinery – featuring the live Xmas turkey, the Mexican tobacco pouch, and over 200 other astounding 'friend of a friend' classics. A glowing testament to the sordid inventiveness of the human mind, this new literary twist on an age-old folk form plumbs the depths of society's irrational prejudices, unquenchable gullibility and sheer stupidity. Spice up any conversation with this fresh and fruity cocktail of comical cautionary tales.

ISBN 0 86369 752 6

THE OFFICIAL POLITICALLY INCORRECT HANDBOOK

Mike Lepine and Mark Leigh

Dare to be politically incorrect! Sick to death of being told to save the world, protect the ozone layer, stop smoking, start exercising, use pooper-scoopers, reassess your materialistic values and insulate the loft? Then this is the book for you – the perfect antidote to the wave of uncontrollable political correctness that has swept the country. This is the book that dares to call a spade a spade – not a 'manual excavatory implement.'

ISBN 0 86369 748 8

GROSS

Karl Shaw

Take a deep breath and plunge into the first compendium of the unspeakable, the unpalatable, the unjust and the appalling. Refreshingly unfettered by good taste, this literary cesspool of grim, grisly but fascinating facts and anecdotes about life, death, sex, filthy lucre and personal hygiene is an indispensable conversation-stopper for a dinner party near you. It could ruin your appetite forever.

ISBN 0 86369 791 7

GROSS 2

Karl Shaw

You thought the first *Gross* was an unbearable journey into the unmentionables? Well listen up – this time it's personal! Enliven the dullest party, amaze your friends and disgust your boss with the kind of knowledge that marks you out as individual, spirited and sick. No social gathering will ever be the same after *Gross 2 . . .*

ISBN 0 86369 896 4

LIFE AT THE TIP

Merv Grist

Life at the Tip is a season's diary in the inglorious life of Les Bence, star of the cult football magazine *When Saturday Comes* and hapless manager of the disastrous Athletico Whaddon. A year is a long time in football – nine months in fact. For Les, each passing year is a life time of hair loss and alcohol consumption watching over his woeful team. As armchair fans salivate over Football Italia and the Premier League, Les hilariously chronicles his season. Irresistible for any football fan.

ISBN 0 86369 613 9